TRAINING WORKHORSES
L. R. Miller
TRAINING TEAMSTERS

First Edition / Second Impression

Author
L. R. Miller

Photographer
All photographs by K. Gilman-Miller
unless otherwise noted

Book Design and Editing
L. R. Miller

Publisher
Small Farmer's Journal Inc.
P.O. Box 1627
Sisters, Oregon 97759

Printer
Maverick Publishing
Bend, Oregon

ISBN 1-885210-00-0

On the front cover: (top) Lynn adjusts the bit for Juniper. (bottom) Red and Blue take their first steps on a mower with Lynn driving. This was their fourth time hitched after "mutual acceptance / round pen training".

On the back cover: Marian Greendale leads Tuck, and Lynn leads Barney, after a day's work on Singing Horse Ranch.

dedication

To Kristi - my partner, my wife, my friend.

aknowledgements

Lots of time went into the making of this book. And I need to thank some forgiving and giving people.

First this book would never have seen the light of day were it not for my wife, Kristi. She gave up quite a bit to see it happen. And she gave an enormous effort towards its completion, as you can see by her hundreds of fine photographs. Without her imagery and steady eye this book would be a ghost of what you hold. She is truly an artist. And she is my partner. Even when I faltered, and threatened to throw in the pencil, she kept me going. She never gave up on me or this book.

And I want to thank my father for his fine foreword, and for raising me to question and prod and care. And thanks go to Chris Ragan and Kathy Blann for typing and proof-reading mountains of material, much of it scribbled in crippled pencil. And thanks to my brother, Tony, for shouldering a load at the ranch while I was trying to get it to the printer. And thanks to my friend, Jess Ross, for volunteering many days over three plus years to help me with the horses. And thanks to the Aden Freeman family for sharing their training story.

But before there was even the idea of this book I got my own rough start with work horses. Were it not for three men, who stopped and picked me up, brushed me off and set me back on my feet, I would not be working horses today. I owe a great debt to Ray Drongeson, Charley Jensen and Howard Steele.

And while I'm at it I would like to take my hat off to a list of teamsters who taught me and inspired me from a distance. I doubt that they ever knew I looked to them as teachers or role models or inspiration. Thank you Monte Rumgay, Herman Daniel, Bob Green, Dan Kintz, Joe Van Dyke, Don McInnis, Willard Lee, Ira Brown, Ferd Mantei, Lloyd Hanson, Gary Eagle, Arnold Hexom, Forest Davis, Jess Ross, Mel Anderson, Cornelius Verduin, Harold McMain, Jack Carver, Jiggs Kinney, Aden Freeman, Jimmy Grant, and John Male. There are others who also belong on this list but I am getting forgetful, if no less appreciative. Also I want to thank two horsemen I've never met except through their words and inspiration. The philosophy and work of Tom Dorrance, and Ray Hunt, gave me the courage to trust my instincts with horses. LRM

Foreword

QUO EQUUS?

Although I have not put my hand on it in a couple of years I'm convinced there still exists a photograph, circa 1919, of this writer, as a very small boy, perched high on the withers of an old brown, harnessed gelding known only and always as simply 'Old Jake'. In illustration it denotes the most widespread beginning of the training of teamsters in that era.

Another horse shown in the picture was Bess, a young black mare about the same age as the boy (3 1/2); she was farm raised, newly broken in and the previous foal of our third animal. Bess was teamed in the photo with Jake but trained by Nell, her mother, from birth. Nell herself was out of the picture momentarily awaiting arrival of another foal. Again the training practice most often practiced in the western world. Small boys and foals simply grew into it. But note that time...

Although few could imagine it, the era of the work horse had just passed its peak. Jake, Nell, Bess and the colt, part of an army of millions, destined to dwindle to a comparative handful over the next 40 to 45 years. How sad it was --!

With their passing went so much and so many of the opportunities for children and foals to be born into the class of teams and teamsters. There were exceptions but pitifully few. Anyone connected to draft horses, work horses, has heard it countless times --, 'My Father - Uncle - Grandfather - farmed with horses.' Yes it's true, they did, but like this writer, WE didn't! At least not for long. We left it behind by millions and most of us never perfected the touch or soon forgot it. I did work horses on and off (more off than on) until I left home at twenty-one and went on to something else.

Fortunately for me, and perhaps for you and posterity, I always regretted it. I remember once in 1960 when trenching with a tractor for a building foundation, a young fellow working for me dug up a trace hook from a single tree and said, "what in the world is that?" It staggered me to think whole generations had grown up with absolutely no knowledge of harnessed horses. Perhaps by some process I passed my wistful, rueful regret on to my son, Lynn.

He represents the other side of teamster experience as expressed in this book and the companion volume "**The Work Horse Handbook**". It is indeed a whole different experience and one which most readers of this volume will share -- to be starting completely from scratch.

If you are just at (or before) the beginning stage you may be thinking that working horses is romantic, mystic, esoteric---; Lynn, having come to it from that approach gives some such indication along with the wholly practical; and more mundane.

Those of us born into it rarely thought of it like that. We absorbed it through our pores and from our chores. Feeding, watering, mucking out, rubbing and currying, some chores were better, some worse. The sights, sounds, and particularly, smells of horses, harness leather, sweat and horse droppings permeated our senses and our days. The team was so much a part or our lives we rarely separated ir from other farm realities.

There could have been both advantage and a detriment to our approach. Admittedly, it comes much easier to have grown up with it but perhaps we took horses too much for granted. Even when we treated them well and gave proper care and feeding, we often ignored any personalities, traits and feelings of a particular animal (except the most fractious ones).

As Lynn indicates and spells out in this volume horses do have individual characteristics and limitations, mental as well as physical, just as we do. Understanding them, taking them into account at every conjuncture makes every aspect of training easier on teams and teamsters alike. "That", to quote the 'melancholy Dane', "is a consumation devoutly to be wished."

Giving or getting advice is nothing new. When we left the farm for a couple of years the house we rented in town had an abandoned stable next to the alley. Up to World War I there may well have been more horses in cities than on farms. Those who didn't keep them rented by day from the livery stable. Driving harnessed horses was the practise not the exception. Although horse workshops and teamster training as an option didn't exist everyone with or without experience was an expert. No test and no license needed; if you ran into difficulties there was no lack of advice. It was a time hard on drivers, drivers widows and particularly the poor horses.

Since that vast pool of experience(?) has virtually disappeared the need for a carefully considered approach is readily apparent. To appreciate and become comfortable with working horses we need both the practical hands on practice and well researched written advice. As the old chestnut has it, "when all else fails read the instructions."

Lynn came by his desire to have and work horses on his own. He got and used advice from the only one he found using horses near him. When it wasn't enough he wrote Maurice Telleen asking for articles in the *Draft Horse Journal*. Telleen's reply made history: 'That's another magazine'. The **Small Farmers Journal** and continued reserach both on his own and among the growing army of teamster aquaintances led to the *"The Work Horse Handbook"*. The Handbook filled a need but generated more questions and more research; hence *"TRAINING WORKHORSES/TRAINING TEAMSTERS"*.

Lynn has never been content with the notion that there is only one way to do anything. He has never minded getting up and explaining or demonstrating his own views, but he is always happier getting a bunch of down to earth practitioners to talk about personal feelings and experiences while he plays moderator, audience or devil's advocate by turns. (He asks not only how but why?) And when he doesn't get all the answers, he researches some more, studies and then works them out by trial and error mixed with generous helpings of 'horse sense'.

He lives with his tightly knit family group on that ranch so far into the back country that even old timers are wont to deny the area exists. (The bank he bought it from couldn't tell him how to get there and he spent two days looking for it.) In that locale he might be taken for a hermit or a recluse, yet people from the entire nation and even worldwide are his constant confidants and correspondents. Horses, work horses, is the password.

One thing a writing guru told me long ago, "Don't try to write about what's interesting; write about what's important." It's a lesson Lynn has learned well. This book like **The Work Horse Handbook** is important. Unlike the conditions at the beginning of this century, those interested in working horses today do it by choice...and for valid reasons. Understanding the human/horse relationship, the why as well as the how of working horses, is a substantial answer to a crying need.

If you read this book carefully, then keep it handy for regular reference, and if it helps you to realization as I'm sure it will, it will not only justify Lynn's work and study but may make up in part for those rueful regrets of those of us who dropped out so long ago.

Ralph Miller
Starke, Florida, February 1994

Ralph Miller and grandson Justin in 1976

TRAINING WORKHORSES /
TRAINING TEAMSTERS
By L. R. Miller

TABLE OF CONTENTS

TRAINING TEAMSTERS

LM 86

INTRODUCTION

You hold in your hands a fairly substantial book, most of which is on a subject that, in the recent past, has been successfully covered by other authors in the form of topical pamphlets. This volume differs from those in that it attempts to offer a more thorough presentation including many approaches to the subject. Efforts have been made, however, to design this volume so that the anxious person may get needed information quickly. For this reason a careful reading of the entire text may uncover repetition. Please excuse this clumsy necessity.

The Revival of the Workhorse

Not so long ago many considered the art of working horses and mules in harness to be a dying craft. It was believed that, when the few hundred remaining old teamsters passed on, the work horse would reside solely as a historical relic; a curiosity, a cultural ghost. Few had envisioned, 25 years ago, that thousands would be drawn to this mode of work and transportation for practical as well as romantic reasons, but they have. Dwindling draft horse numbers have done an about face, with every breed showing substantial growth. Now, in corners all across North America, you can see workhorses and mules plowing, logging, mowing, hauling, seeding, and harvesting crops. Today over 200,000 people have chosen to depend on the workhorse or mule. Cottage industries have sprung up all across North America to support what has become an unexpected phenomenon, the revival of the work horse. Every indication is that this is not a fad or passing fanciful flirtation with the near past. It is a solid rebuilding of the architecture of the concept of, and feasibility of, work horses and mules as a motive power option, because many of us see the place, the need, and the value of the work horse in the modern world. And this revival is not an empty threat by a few fanatics to replace internal combustion. It is the dedication of many sensible, thoughtful, intelligent folk to the preservation, development and application of a humane modern animal power source as a reasonable option for today

In this revival business we, as the draft animal industry, are evolving onto a plateau, or what I believe to be a second stage of growth (an indication that this is not a fad). With some years behind us, and many patterns available to suggest trends, or problems, or hope, many are concerned that future growth depends on better educated teamsters and better trained animals.

It is true that many people came to this subtle and complex business of work horses ill-prepared, with nothing but high expectations and no experience. And that far too many of these newcomers were met with horrible or unfortunate first experiences which soured them to the craft. This was tragically unnecessary.

Our work, with the quarterly **SMALL FARMER'S JOURNAL** and other publications such as **The WORK HORSE HANDBOOK**, has been dedicated in no small way to the needs of newcomers because of our belief that they represent an opportunity to shape a better tomorrow for WORK HORSES.

This book is aimed, in part, at these newcomers. This text is not written specifically as a handbook for the inexperienced to train their own horses. I hold that people inexperienced with horses should not attempt to train them. It would be ideal to imagine that any who read this come with a fair measure of teamster experience but we must be realistic. Those most hungry for information will be those who come fresh and inexperienced. So I have attempted to present two texts wrapped into one, hopefully addressing the needs of several catagories, none the least of which is the newcomer.

The author discing weeds with Belgian mares, Cali and Lana.

In watching this work horse revival, we have seen one curious phenomenon that could be viewed as either unfortunate or hopeful. I am speaking of a segment of the work horse community that I might refer to as the "Holders." These good folk came, inexperienced, to work horses with dreams so large and strong that bad first experiences could not shake them. They have held onto the dream that work horses would work, eventually, for them. But human nature and things what they are, these "holders" have not found the trustworthy efficient, practical world of work horses, yet. They might continue, clumsy and/or frightened, or they might simply wait, but one thing is certain for them - they are missing key elements that make animal power work. They need help in finding those elements. They get easily frustrated when they see others "enjoy" the ease and comfort and efficiency of work horses, things which escape them, things they need. They want to be able to trust their animals and enjoy real practicality. I view this as hopeful because these people are, however predisposed to trouble, ripe for the kind of experiences and information that can turn them around and head them off to success. They

14

have experience, it's just that too much of it is either unnecessarily disjointed or it is incomplete. I sincerely hope that this text offers even just one "holder" a bit of good fresh direction and possibility.

This work horse revival is bright because we have so very many exceptional "new" teamsters, "used" teamsters, "seasoned" teamsters, any way you put it - include them all and call them "teamsters." Whether they work horses, drive them for pleasure or show them, these people know what they are doing, they enjoy success. And they deserve the continued improvement in their horses that they all wish for. Hopefully this text may serve, in its organization and presentation, to help them, in some small way, improve their relationship with the horse as a first step in seeing the horse improve.

This work horse revival business has spawned yet another small group which we think of as advocates and "teachers." They can't help but push the beauty and practicality of the horse or mule in harness and in willing service. And many do excellent work helping hundreds of newcomers and holders to find ways to proceed. It is hoped that this small effort will prove of some organizational value to these important people.

This book is written for the "teachers," the "teamsters," the "holders" and the "newcomers," all of the world of the work horse.

Mowing at Singing Horse Ranch, L.R. Miller and Jess Ross.

The Organization of This Book

As important a topic as this is you would do well to demand some references from this author.

I do not claim to be a great trainer of work horses. In fact I am not a trainer in any formal sense. I do have a skill for, and some experience with, communicating and teaching. My work for many years (since 1975) in starting and editing **SMALL FARMER'S JOURNAL** *(featuring Practical Horsefarming)* has brought me into contact and dialogue with tens of thousands of working horse farmers. In 1980 I authored the companion text to this one, **The WORK HORSE HANDBOOK**. For most of these last fifteen years our own horsefarming venture has operated as an adjunct to **Small Farmers' Journal** providing us with a rich ongoing research lab to constantly experiment with applied Horse-Power. And those efforts include

15

long range inquiries into training variables. All this coupled with nearly 20 years of shared work with good horses has led me to many observations and a few conclusions.

Getting some simple, hopefully obvious, definitely important, things out of the way:

I love horses.

I appreciate their patience with me.

I am hugely grateful for what they have given me.

And I like to believe I am on their side.

If you are looking for a simple outline of a quick method for starting a horse in harness you may wonder why this book has to be so thick. Many "quick methods" are in here. And they join longer slower methods along with lots of suggested approaches to specific concerns and problems, because it is my wish to attempt to provide a fairly complete compilation of any usable information on the subject. In this way the horse is better served. This training book effort is a combination of authorship and editing as I have drawn on the expertise of many exceptional horsemen with differing approaches.

The organization of this book perhaps needs a little explaining. First off, I'll say that successful communication of the subject - training work horses - was constantly on my mind. I can't see much value in producing another dust-covered, hard-to-read, pile of gibberish. I have better things to do, most particularly working horses. And you have better things to do - like coming up with answers. So I've put some time (5 years) and thought into how to organize this book and what to include.

I have, as evidenced above, thought about who might read such a book, and what they would need from it. And I am mindful of the great disagreements that exist about "breaking" and "training" - many of which I consider to be semantic arguments or just people determined to disagree. Having strong feelings about ideal relationships with horses, how to get there, and looking out after the animal's interests - there is no way I can keep these things from being a big part of this writing. Yet, to paraphrase

> *"The more I work with horses the less I know and the easier it gets."*

my late, good friend Ray Drongesen, "The more I work with horses the less I know and the easier it gets."

For me this translates to a genuine wonder. I wonder if I really understand what I'm doing. I wonder and marvel at my success. I wonder about my failings. I wonder why more people aren't working horses. I wonder how some folks can be so callous and cruel yet manage to keep their animals working. And sometimes I wonder how, after all these years, I can't seem to make it all work as well as I might imagine. And I wonder how there could be any doubt about our "natural" relations with the equine. All this wondering is what has driven me to include in this text, primarily in the section called "Training Glossary," information that might go contrary to my own philosophies. I believe that it is important to understand all sides in order to fully comprehend whatever may be the chosen side. There is no inherent danger in a full understanding of how to rig a **running W** and what it does when used in different situations.

Understanding will take you closer to a constructive, humble, compassionate effectiveness than will ignorance which so often breeds prideful arrogance. On the subject of variables; I have always held that there is NO only way to do anything. Although we may be risking some confusion I feel the variety will lead to greater understanding, so I have included an

> *Understanding will take you closer to a constructive, humble, compassionate effectiveness than will ignorance, which so often breeds prideful arrogance.*

assortment of different training systems under the heading **Training System Variations**.

How to Use This Book

If anyone were to ask of my preference in how this book is used I would hazard to suggest that it be used four ways.

First, flip through the entire book and look at the diagrams and pictures.

Second, read the first six chapters in their entirety.

Third, pour over chapters seven through fourteen to determine what specifically applies to you and work out how you may use it, CAREFULLY.

Fourth, go through chapter fourteen, "Training Variations", and adjust you rconclusions accordingly.

No doubt some will go straight to what they need or want with no look at the remainder. We can only hope they are schooled enough not to hurt the horse or themselves.

Some will quickly find what they vehemently disagree with, regardless of whether it be out of context, and rush to condemn. Not much can be said about this except that it comes with the territory.

Why Use This Book

A brief aside about the territory of horsekeepers: After all these years I have still not managed to muster much patience or compassion for the segment of the horse industry, so often tied to the show ring but certainly not restricted to it, who are the arrogant, elitist, snobbish, users of horse flesh. They extend into all corners from Arabian horses, to Walking horses, to Quarter horses, to Ponies and even well into the ranks of Draft horses. There is one common thread I have found amongst these people - they share a fear of the horse coupled with an often disguised lack of self-confidence. This pushes them to over-compensate with a display of horse control and a stuffy elitistism towards other people. They bother me so because of the good horses they abuse (and have ruined) and because of the negative effect they have on new people.

At the core of their problem lies the belief that horses are dangerous dumb animals who can only attain perfection if beat, tied, chained and coerced into form. It is sad to reflect that it may be too late to show these people that horses are a sublime animal, quite different from us but certainly not inferior, and that they can work with us as well as a willing dance partner might (as Ray Hunt and Tom Dorrance have shown us).

And a good dance requires give and take on both sides. You don't get a good dance with a pushy, arrogant bully. And you don't get a good dance with a frightened, enslaved partner. Traditionally, ballroom dancing is seen to have a leader (the male) and a follower (the female). But in truth we know that much difficulty lies with the female's role as she must understand or anticipate direction and work to have all motion flow together. In a good dancing partnership the female may easily be the superior half without receiving due credit. Working with horses is like this. We have the lead and they follow - yet, given half a chance to enjoy and contribute the horse will add subtlety, depth, range, beauty and ease of motion by anticipation and reaction at fine levels we are often incapable of feeling.

The above might sound like some description of dressage and hardly fitting the needs and concerns of one who wants to plow with their horses. But the point is that, athletic capabilities differing, all horses share the sensitivity that allows, if we are open, for a calm, confident and wonderfully subtle working relationship. You don't need to yell at them, or hit them. You can whisper to them, you can touch them, and they will move for you.

If you doubt what I am trying to say, someday watch a truly exceptional cutting horse perform and measure for yourself the rider's contribution against the horse's. The best cutters realize the horse has a level of perception that is quicker and finer than their own. They must try to stay with the animal without getting in the way. The horse, if allowed, is busy reading the cow and positioning itself to prevent it from passing.

If you have the opportunity, measure the above performance against one where the rider insists on making all decisions and not allowing the horse to move without direction. It will become apparent to you that the horse has much to contribute and we have much to learn.

Training Teamsters

This writing is actually two books in one. Book Two, entitled "**TRAINING TEAM-STERS**" is guided by some very specific experiences. Back in the seventies Ray Drongesen and I evolved a structured training program to introduce people to work horses. The format, in its final form, was modified or customized and applied throughout the U.S. and Canada with excellent results. It is this experience, with Work Horse Workshops, that has convinced me that we can all learn, from a structured, shared environment, much that will help us as Teamsters.

The subtitle of this book would suggest more than just a chapter of the same name.

That is why there is a whole second book included with this training horses text. Perhaps I might even confess to lacing the entire text with efforts to affect the teamster if I weren't concerned that many would put the book down. It is enough to say that I do believe learning how to train work horses will make of us better teamsters.

As a final aside: I have attempted to be thorough in this text, however, there is much you should know, or have access to, that is not here. This is why we recommend this as a companion text to **The WORK HORSE HANDBOOK** and why we include a list of related materials in the back of the book.

I sincerely hope that this effort we call a book will help you and your horses work calmly, confidently, and enjoyably together.

Lynn R. Miller
Singing Horse Ranch

Chapter One

Why Work Horses?

The Teamster's craft is mystery, magic, slight of hand.

Imagine the little man apparently so much in control of the big horses. The man is "civilized," "intelligent," and predictable. The horses are dumb, wild animals tricked to momentary submission.

He is so frail and yet effective of mind, they the exact opposite. The horses are capable of trampling him into a dust stain yet he controls the elements of applied fear.

Compare the word picture above to the one below.

They moved together so smoothly it was hard to tell who was leading except that the pair of large horses walked ahead of the man. The horses matched his speed, as well as each other's, in a calm yet watchful stride. The man's touch on the lines was as soft and subtle as his voice when he spoke, thanking his working friends for making his own efforts easier and pleasureable.

What we choose to see, in this business of work horses, will set up our expectations.

If we see something to crave we will work, subconsciously, to put ourselves in that picture and be also craved by others.

If we see something to fear and therefore master and control we will work for that.

If, however, we enjoy a perception of beauty, comfort, ease and effectiveness we will work to make those our own.

We must understand our motives before we can have a good chance for an enjoyed success.

What we do is important to us.

How we do what we do is more important.

For example: If what we do is farm, that is an important distinction. But how we farm is more important because it includes such critical elements as decisions about toxic chemicals and the preservation of genetic diversity. Most people have no problem accepting these distinctions or statements. But many get confused with the next step ...

Why we do what we do is most important of all.

To continue the metaphor: If we farm in order to make as much money as possible we have, in place, the structure to determine how we farm (and eventually "if" we farm). If we farm not for maximum profit but for intangible reasons that speak of a concern for life and the quality of living we have changed the stakes, and how we proceed reflects, purely, why we proceed.

It is for this reason that I insist on beginning this book about Training Work Horses with a chapter entitled "Why Work Horses?"

There is a cluster of oft-repeated arguments favoring work horses which include these statements:

Work horses are a self-renewing power source which depends on readily available home grown produce for fuel.

Work horses as motive power can be far less expensive than conventional tractor systems.

Work horses lend themselves well to intelligent diversification and interrelated

Aden Freeman and John Male, exceptional teamsters from Ontario, Canada, with four abreast on a stoneboat.

systems on the farm and off.

Work horses are a highly tractable and flexible power source.

Work horses are easy on the farm and forest environs.

Work horses can be easy on people.

During an age when we are occasionally reminded how dependent we are on processed fossil fuels for our very existence, there is a heavy foreboding for Western civilizations. Can we continue, can we survive, when the oil wells come up empty? Who will be able to afford the technology and fuels of the future? The politics and economics of this projected question are crime, devastation, and civil war. Maybe it will never happen, perhaps some competing scientists and inventors will design an entire new way to mine the earth, suck up her juices, and feed humanity's lust for ease and convenience. But it will surely be a short-lived program with perhaps an even higher price tag, a billing against our fragile environment.

Young Canadian teamster discing.

This is a large matter which may not seem to have much relationship to working horses but it surely does. The problem suggested above is not that we may be short of petroleum products. The problem is that so-called civilized humankind has become lazy. We, many of us, have traded our individual physical and spiritual capabilities for a chance at a life of "comfort," "easy thrills," "pain-lessness," and "convenience." And those four commodities, for which we have given up true freedom, are the very same things a drug addict is finding briefly with his or her poison. After the drug wears off - or when the condo dweller turns off the television and accidently sits with life measuring solitude - the person first realizes he or she has been nowhere, done nothing. The first realization, however short, is of a deathly waste. And immediately comes a terror that many feel can only be treated by more of the drug, more of the deadening.

What do I feel after a hard day of working with my horses? I feel blessed. I feel, in that moment of life measuring solitude, like I have been somewhere, done something, felt my capabilities, learned something, and shared something. I feel useful, capable, needed, and comically insignificant. I feel both pride and humanity. I feel like expanding this world of good work. I feel like adjusting the plow, patching the harness, currying the horses some more. I feel like my ability to get the work done is truly that - my ability. And I wonder why more people have not found this.

Working horses is a small, some may say silly, idea measured against these enormous questions of petroleum dependency, environmental concerns, and collective spiritual health. But it is at this bottom level that these questions must be addressed. Work horses are a single small specialized optional power source that represents a microcosm of a much larger question of the human condition. And that question is: "What will humankind do with its existence?"

We all know the answer but most of us fear it. We need to feel good about ourselves, enjoy our work, work hard at it

The author plowing with a walking plow and three abreast.

and understand how we live without polluting and mining. Doesn't sound so bad, so why do we fear it? Because it means leaving behind that drugging convenience. It means trading aerobics, jogging and T.V. for the physical efforts of real work. It means trading in motor homes for tents. It means trading tractors for horses and mules. It means trading an external job security for an internal one.

The idea of work horses as motive power for the farm is a benign notion. You wouldn't think people would be angered or threatened by the suggestion - but many are. You'd think it would be more common for uninterested or disagreeing folk to smile and push the argument aside as if it were nonsense. But instead many rush to find the statistical ammo to try to shoot down the idea. I choose to consider this response an indication of how close we are to a truth and how our culture feels compelled to defend the lies of its transfigured and polluted mandate. That mandate used to be to improve the human condition while protecting basic rights. In the beginning a valued understanding and respect of dignity, self-reliance and humility as basic truth was generally taken as granted. That is gone now - replaced by arrogance, self-indulgence and nihilism. And improvements in the human condition are measured as some mechanical sizing of standardof-living or increased affluence. Meanwhile, the real human condition, as measured in terms of whole health, self-respect and true security, worsens each day.

Given the modern world I suppose it is no wonder that the teamster's craft would be viewed as either nonsense or pure magic. And what is magic, really, but something partially hidden from view or understanding. So I say yes, the teamsters craft at its best is most definitely magic. And this craft is like some secret society loaded with private skills. You don't just sign up to belong, you'll not meet any directors. And the initiation rites go on non-stop. The premiums of membership, which come only with acquired facility, are difficult to describe but truly wondrous. And one thing is for certain, from the inside this teamster business is no-nonsense.

And here's a place to say, in bold type:

The Teamster's craft can be terribly dangerous for any who come unschooled and arrogant.

Dangerous for obvious reasons - if frightened large animals are convinced they must protect themselves or escape, your response is critical. You can't remedy the situation by determination, physical strength or displays of anger. In fact ...

You don't need to be quick, strong or aggressive to work horses.

Because the best relationship with a work horse comes from understanding the animal, it comes from patience and a consistent, soft contact.

This translates to the fact that anyone who is open to learn and adjust will do just fine as a teamster. But there are many who might fit that description yet have no interest in the animals, may not even like them. They have no business getting involved in work horses. The horses and mules deserve better.

Charlie Jensen of Oregon plowing with three Percherons abreast.

Before internal combustion engines, when animal power was just about everything, the dray beast had a mostly terrible existence. No doubt there were notable exceptions, but people had little choice. That translated to the fact that many of the people driving and riding horses didn't like them and were not especially skilled at handling them. The animals were horribly abused and neglected and yet they still did the work that developed this western civilization.

Today we have many choices. Few of us are "stuck" with work horses or mules. That bodes well for the animals because not only are people making a conscious choice to work with them, but they are looking for instruction. This converts, often, to good, kind, just homes for draft animals if these newcomers get sound help.

Work horses and mules, in today's fast paced modern world, can do important valued work in many areas. Typically we think about them as a power source on the farm. And, of course, they fit wonderfully into recreation. But they are also dynamic options for work skidding forest products from areas we wish to protect. (Shouldn't we protect it all?) They have continued to prove themselves as transportation for goods and people in traffic-clogged city centers. And there are exciting applications everywhere (such as the treadmill-powered vegetable cleaning plant in Kentucky) that speak to the notion we champion, which is that imagination and caring are all that is needed to devise an unlimited array of new applications for a humane animal power.

Bud Dimick, of Oregon, mowing with his Percheron team.

But certainly, where the work horse excels is back home on the farm. And not necessarily one of today's monocultural factory farms. The horse and mule are best put to work on diversified mixed crop and livestock operations where work schedules and crop residues allow extremely efficient use of the animals. It is possible on some such farms to cover a third or half of the work-animal feed requirements with crop residues and waste area pasturing. Yet, lest we sound like we need to excuse the feed consumption of the animals think about two things:

Leonard Mothersbaugh, of Missouri, with his six abreast of Belgians discing.

1) Home-grown feed stuffs fed to work horses that power that same farm makes excellent economic sense as a closed circle of cost efficient self-reliance;

2) Our massive crop surpluses came into being exactly at the time when tractors replaced horses and mules. Crop surpluses are the single biggest reason that farm commodity prices have been so poor for so long.

If surpluses were fed to our motive power source, eliminating or reducing the cost of petro products, and farm commodity prices went up, the general farm economy would look excellent.

And the work horse is self-renewing. Might not seem like a big point until you remember that tractors need to be replaced. Horses have babies to replace themselves. In fact, horses often have more babies than are required for replacement. Sale of those "surplus" horses adds to the farm's balance of payments. The replacement of tractors costs the farm community hundreds of millions of dollars. The replacement of work horses NETS the farm community millions of dollars.

It isn't necessary to dwell on the difference in initial cost of work horses versus tractors. You can do your own comparisons. It is perhaps enough to say that good, common, well-trained horses have been purchased for $700 or $1,000 each. But their cost efficiency must be measured in total, taking into consideration the contributions made as well as all costs incurred.

Remember that besides the work considerations, each horse is a fertilizer factory producing up to seven tons per year of valuable manure.

And remember that work horses are a public attractant which, if creatively utilized, can enhance direct sales of farm produce.

One of the aspects of work horses that I have personally learned to value is the unique flexibility of the system. With eight head of work horses we can put them all together, in one

The author cleaning his pond with Molly and Barney.

hitch, and plow or disc or harrow. Then we can divide them up and put two teams on seed drills and a third team on a packer-roller. Come harvest time we can put four teams on mowers, in the beginning, and drop up to 40 acres of hay in one day. Then we can put two teams on rakes leaving two on mowers. Then on the third day we can have one team mowing, one team raking, and two teams bucking hay or baling or whatever. You can use any combination you need for the appropriate equipment. That's hard to do when you have one big 100 hp, 4-wheel drive tractor.

And that tractor I've just mentioned does something to your soil that you ought to know about. Driving that beast back and forth across the field, the tires compact the soil just below the tillage depth. So seven to ten inches down, where you can't see it, you've used a rolling pin action on that subsoil that is restricting water and root penetration.

Work horses and mules, walking across the tilled soil, have many points of contact, rather than the rolling pin action of the tractor tires, and do not compact the soil in a sheet. Rather the shifting plate action of each hoof serves to open the ground.

Work horses and mules are far gentler to our soils, be they forest or farm, than are tractors. If you ever have an opportunity to visit a logged off area where vehicles are used and then compare that with one where horses did the work you will see wholesale destruction versus what looks like animal trails in a park.

The author on the disc.

We've gone round about but we certainly haven't touched on every possible reason why to use work horses. It is important to repeat the suggestion that why you work them will certainly affect the outcome. The animal power business should not be viewed as a simple linear replacement for modern power systems. As we've hinted, work horses will try to affect your operation systems, apply some intelligence and an open mind and take

27

a chance with the direction it wants to take you. Within this is a possiblity for a pleasurable working environment and greater real profit.

Remember that profit is supposed to be simple money math: Subtract what you put in from what you get back. If you put in 99 and get back 100 your profit is one. If you put in 20 and get back 60 your profit is 40. In abstract these numbers relate to horses vs. tractors. It is certainly true that farming with horses allows you to keep more of what you make. And if your gross receipts are less what difference does it make if your net profit is more. That margin is a measure of self-reliance.

And self-reliance builds true self-esteem. Which brings me to this closing notion: Work horses and mules can be easy on people.

Well-trained, confident, calm draft animals working for a teamster they respect is a wonderfully correct power unit of tremendous effectiveness. And it is an easy and reassuring work for the skilled person - no matter the physical stature or strength.

But the word picture above requires two things: Well-trained horses and a skilled teamster. It is true that a skilled teamster can make the well-trained horses. It is not true that well-trained horses can make a skilled teamster. They can certainly help. But the countryside is littered with the remains of well-trained horses that were spoiled, injured or killed by inexperienced well-wishing newcomers. We want that to stop today. It is an unnecessary and tragic waste.

A book like this is one small sincere effort to make the best possibilities come true for you. And if that's why you want to work horses - for all the best possibilities - keep your mind, and all the senses that feed it, open - we'll try to send some good stuff your way.

Welcome to something that might change your whole life.

John Male, of Ontario, Canada, on the walking plow.

28

*This book is about smart horses with courage,
and the humility and sensitivity required
of humans to keep their horses that way.*

Chapter two

Understanding Horses

As was mentioned before, **The WORK HORSE HANDBOOK** is meant to be referred to as a companion volume to this text. Within the chapter in WHHB entitled "ATTITUDE and APPROACH" is a discussion about the psychology and sensory perception of horses which covers, in brief, what we must cover, throughout this text, in a little greater detail.

Adaptability & Intelligence

It is my sincere belief that successful training of work horses begins with a comprehensive understanding of the horse. But there is an implicit paradox with this as I also believe that our ability to know the horse is limited and based, at best, on a lot of guess work.

Our historical record of success with horses, given a myriad of applied theories, reinforces my conviction that these animals have a sublimely complex and advanced capacity for adaptability. Think about it - they can survive well in the wild or in New York City (although the wild is perhaps better for them). They perform reasonably well for the horse abusers and for the unschooled beginner. Patience is their hallmark even though flight appears to be their first tool of defense. And flight suggests a low panic threshold. Stallions, while protecting mare bands in the wild, have repeatedly demonstrated fox-like skills for understanding how they might outsmart pursuers. And given an opportunity for a relationship of mutual trust and admiration, the team of human and horse has done some incredible things - even to affecting history. If we can agree that the horse, as a rule, is highly adaptable, can we also agree that this would point to a measureable intelligence?

I can feel some of you backing away. I recognize that for all of man's history the prevalent feeling has been that horse's are dumb animals. What for many people, has

differentiated them from us is the embraced notion that we are intelligent and they are not.

Please bear with me on this for a little bit.

The dictionary definition of "intelligence" includes:

The faculty of understanding.

"Intelligent" includes:

Having a good understanding or a high mental capacity; quick to comprehend, as persons or animals.

Now back to my point about adaptability: In order to display the capacity to adapt horses must clearly perceive something to react to. They must "understand" that such and such is a threat, or reward, or required motion. Whether or not their "understanding" is correct is purely subjective on our part and cannot be taken as a determination of the intelligence. Who is to say that we are right in our perception of what should be a correct understanding. This is a key component, one of the most important elements, in the quest for truly effective training. I will return to this point repeatedly but let's make it here, first.

If in a new relationship with a horse you have chosen a reaction you want from the animal and you have "decided" that a certain action on your part should result in compliance you have proven the horse to be of superior intelligence to your own. You see, you have made a presumption and the horse has not. You are prepared to enforce your presumption while the horse simply waits for a clear signal to decide on action. The horse is working towards understanding. You've decided you already know the answer and have closed the doors to something new or different. Someone who is closed to understanding is, by definition, lacking in intelligence.

Most horses are always open to understanding except when lost to deep panic. This is more than can be said of most humans.

While on the subject, perhaps a backside view will help convey the thought. I started that last paragraph by saying, "If in a NEW rela-
tionship ..." It was with good reason because the point would have or could have been clouded by an example of a long-standing relationship. Many teamsters, holders and new comers have not cred-
ited their horses with much intelligence and the animals have retrofitted their apparent compliancy with a closed notion about their handler. If you can believe this, what I am saying is that the animals develop a prejudice about their handlers to a greater or lesser degree depending on the sensitivity of the handler! In other words, your horse may have decided, long ago, that you aren't all that smart and that the best your horse could expect was fair treatment if it followed your confusing directions.

"Don", an exceptionally intelligent gelding which belonged to Aden Freeman of Ontario, Canada

Imagine that. I am suggesting that we have enjoyed a fair measure of success with horses over several hundred (perhaps a thousand) years primarily because of the intelligence and adaptability of the animals. And, one important step further, clearly what has prevented most people from a truly exceptional working relationship with "TRUSTING" horses is the human mind closed to understanding, closed to adaptation, closed to intelligence.

Now, just when you might understand, or think you understand, what I'm trying to say hear this: HORSES CAN BE SO BLANKITY, BLANK STUPID! The above curse can certainly be a legitimate, honest reactive statement. But it is only constructively so if put into proper context.

Horses are stupid to us when we can't seem to convince them of what it is we want. Or when, our influence removed, they seem bent on some self-destruction - getting cut up in wire - or bloating on grain - or running out onto a busy highway. Stupid animals! Or are they?

There are inherent behavioral characteristics which appear to be held in common by most animals (humans included). Within all species there are great differences of intelligence, self-motivation and athletic ability from one individual to another. The greater the degree of any combination of these three elements found in an individual animal (include humans) the greater the independence of action and spirit demonstrated. The closer to the median or

31

average of these three elements the more inclined the individual will be to find comfort and direction in numbers of its own kind. And the more susceptible it will be to direct supervision. This is to say that the majority of horses being relied upon are most likely those of common intelligence, athletic ability and self-motivation. The truly exceptional animals pose too much of a challenge to most of us to presume training. And it is because we view them as behavioral problems rather than examples of great intelligence.

It all comes down on one leg, to our unwillingness to see it as intelligence. And, on the other leg, to our denial of our own capabilities.

They are not stupid. We are, for insisting on measuring them with some screwed up human (parental) yardstick that equates compliance with smarts.

"You should've known better!"

"What's got into your head? Don't you realize that you ...!"

"You know perfectly well what I mean!"

These statements represent confused sentiments we've all felt whether as the speaker or the recipient. It's confusing as heck to try to figure out what is expected of us when a parent or teacher, out of frustration, throws these barbed generalities our way. And the parent is also confused in his or her frustration, being unable to come up with some really concise, clear statement or reaction. Understanding is out the window. We leap, with the

grip of the moment, at the hope that a good shake up is all it takes to line out the mess. It might give us a brief sense of confined energy that we translate to be a correction. But it isn't a correction. It's a denial that reduces effectiveness cummulatively with each occurance. In time, this repeated trade-off of the quick convenience of contrived control will breakdown all communication and make cooperative efforts uncomfortable at best, and impossible at worst. And I am talking here about something which applies directly to our time with horses.

The author on the stoneboat with Cali & Lana. Photo by Dayna Tomaselli

A few paragraphs back I attempted to make a distinction between average horses and exceptional ones with the suggestion that the brighter the animal the more difficult the training. And before that I talked about the frustration we feel when any horse doesn't or won't do what's expected (or best?) for him or her. How we rush to label it as stupid. These two points are related in that they come out of the same problem attitude of humans. At the core is our simplistic presumption that all we can expect (or the best we can anticipate) is submission from horses. That is to say that they should - will - must - can - do what we want without quarrel (certainly without thinking). Well, it is not that simple. I argue that earning a willing compliance, rather than extricating submission, results in a far superior work mate. And the only thing required of us to accomplish this is the right attitude - an attitude born of a never-ending quest for understanding. An attitude open to sensitivity and empathy. An attitude with very little room for locked-in conclusions. I argue

Tony Miller drives Barney and Molly on the side delivery rake.

that we can train the smarter horses easier than we can the average ones by carrying the right attitude. And that these will make the best work mates for us. Later we'll talk about what distinguishes a "lead" horse from a "wheeler." Enough to say here that my goal is to have all "leaders" of the best sort. But all this begins with the willingness, even urgency, to accept the possibility that if we ever feel the horse is stupid, the problem may be with us.

The author checks Cali's harness adjustments.

33

THE SENSE OF THE HORSE

I've argued that the horse is an intelligent animal in ways quite different from us. It's time to talk about what we know of the sense of the horse, to try to understand how their intelligence differs.

The windows or doors to our mind and spirit are our eyes, ears, nose, mouth, outer layer (meaning more than skin), and thoughts (imagination). The same is true with horses.

When I speak of windows and doors I am thinking in broad terms. I mean to include that these are portals through which we, and they, receive stimuli. I mean to include that these are passage-ways through which we might glimpse something of the nature of one another. (And, yes, I included "thoughts" with good reason.)

Smell

The equine has an extremely acute sense of smell. The large surface area of its nostrils surely contribute. It has been regularly demonstrated that horses can pick up smells that we do not. But perhaps more important - horses are always prepared to make a speedy determination and response to a threatening and/or unknown odor. And, conversely, understanding this we can accustom horses to specific smells thereby helping them to overcome what might be, in our controlled environment, a bothersome restriction.

An example: If a horse has been raised and trained without ever having been in the presence of hogs and is then introduced to a miniscule particle of hog odor the horse will refuse to proceed anywhere near. The teamster can attempt to remove the odor or choose to go the long way around it. Or the teamster can work to accustom the horse to the odor, gradually and in secure familiar surroundings.

Kristi Gilman-Miller getting sniffed by Singing Horse Ranch Belgians. Photo by L.R. Miller

With patience the horse can be expected to "learn" to accept the odor. If, however, we insist on beating or coercing the frightened, confused horse to pass through the unfamiliar odor we have inadvertently compounded the problem. The horse will now associate the strange odor with an unpleasant

34

struggle.

You might think that, because you have no hogs, your horse is unaccustomed to the odor. But the smell can carry in a breeze from several miles and, although too weak for you to catch, be a regular part of the horse's sensory world.

In Victorian England many stories were told of how crafty older teamsters used their understanding of the equine sense of smell to trick younger horsemen into believing that magic ruled supreme. The strategically concealed placement of a concentrated drop of some intense, strange odor could be expected to cause the best trained horses to stop dead in their tracks. Removal of the odor (say with a tray of warm milk as absorbent) would magically remove the restrictive spell from the horse.

Rather than seeing the sense of smell in horses as a curiosity to be manipulated, please consider it as it is; a wonderfully acute sensory capability devised as part of an early warning defense mechanism.

As a last example: I once lived on a farm surrounded by dense forest. When I first moved there my horses - all from strictly farm environs with no forest experience - seemed generally worried. I watched one day when all the horses in one field immediately turned to look towards one corner of the woods. As a unit they ran to the opposite corner. About 15 minutes passed and their attention remained riveted. Then I saw a small black bear amble along next to the fence for a second and then disappear into the woods. After this the horses started to graze and wander.

Cali resting during a buck raking day at Singing Horse Ranch.

Seven years later, on the same farm, the horse herd included a few of the same animals and several born and raised there. One morning, about 200 feet from the house, we saw a large black bear walking in circles in the swamp that was part of the horse pasture. The horses were all around the bear and several were making striking, squealing advances. Through binoculars it appeared the bear had some damage to his face. I feared perhaps a horse kick. I called the horses over to the next pasture and shut the gate. They seemed a little excited, but certainly not frightened.

(Footnote: I called the game police and when they arrived, two hours later, we had determined the bear was either blind or out of its head. There was no evidence of a horse having kicked the bear. Lab tests on the dead bear indicated it was dying of a fever and infection probably connected to a previous injury to the eye.)

I give the above example to point out that there are ways we can observe how the equine sense of smell (coupled with other sensory perception) serves to warn the animals of the proximity or advance of unknown elements (the bear) so that the horse might flee to safety. But the same senses, married to the equine capacity for understanding, can work over time to allow the horses to determine that the bears are another element of the environment. I don't mean to suggest that the horses came to believe that all bears pose no threat. I do believe, however, that the horses became comfortable with their own ability to determine the relative hazard of a given bear at a given time. And this is the most important distinction because it once again points to regular, natural capacity for reasoned judgement (our "definition" of intelligence).

A rolling stallion

In the wild horses appear to be able to judge, by scent, the relative proximity of an "understood" threat. In other words, men on horseback may well be judged and understood as a threat to "feral" or wild horses. It has been demonstrated that wild horses have determined, by smell, that men were approaching but did not choose to flee until such time as those men crossed some invisible barrier which seemed to scream "close enough."

Twenty-five years ago a Cherokee friend of mine recounted to me of his boyhood work, rounding up wild horses in Nevada and herding them across the mountains to California. He said:

"Horses can smell you before they hear you. And they can hear you before they see you. And they can see you before they feel you or taste you.

"If they haven't tasted or felt man yet they are easy to herd because their fear over-rules their judgement.

"If they have tasted man they are much harder to herd because they are sure of their own cleverness. They will wait until you get too close and then they will move just far enough away. They will break from the herd, if need be, because they know their own strength. While the frightened ones stay close together and run away from you. They are easy to herd, too scared to think. But the horse who has tasted man, the one who is hard to catch and harder to herd, he is the one I want because he has taught himself to

36

think and he acts on fear, he does not react to fear. He is a smart horse with courage."

It might be off the subject of smell but it is a good place to say that this book is about smart horses with courage and the humility and sensitivity required of humans to keep their horses that way.

We can allow our horses to be SMART. And we can teach our horses courage.

Hearing

We're looking for general understanding so we aren't going to get into a lot of technical language in describing horses. For example, I'd like you to think about the horse as having furry radar dishes attached to the top of its head. And each dish can rotate about 300 degrees. (Any more and they'd unscrew and fall off!) These dishes can rotate in parallel unison or independent of one another. They are extremely sensitive and capable of discerning sounds which are far above and below the audio registery of human ears. These dishes are the horses ears. And they, including the incredible caverns of the connected inner ear, account for the horse being able to hear things we can't hear.

The author's Belgian stallion, Abe, listening.

They are part of an early warning system serving the wild horse. Strange noises, or ones connected, by experience, to pain or unpleasantness will cause the horse to "consider" escape. Familiar noises connected to pleasant memories will cause curiosity at least and approach at best. In a fully domesticated willing equine partner trust supplants many primal responses to unusual and threatening noises with a cautious attentive curiosity.

The well trained horse, one which has been "taught" courage and allowed intelligence, can with its human teammate go into bizarre and frightening places with a quick and sure demeanor.

Imagine with me, for a minute, that you had lived your entire life in the woods or on a farm and had never been to the city. Now close your eyes and think of what it would be like to walk the streets of downtown New York City at rush hour. A staggering array of noises and sights and threats and bumps coming at you from EVERY direction!

Or...

Imagine you are pushed through doors into a huge covered arena, blinding lights above, tens of thousands of people sitting all around, hitting themselves, staring at you, and screaming, and horrible organ music wafting below a loud speaker announcing your entry. It gives me the shakes to think about it!

Yet I have described two things horses are regularly subjected to. And they are fully capable of an excellent, courageous, intelligent, calm response to these very environments. Amazing!

Van Seeney, of Oregon, drives his handsome four-up of Mules in a Prineville parade. Well behaved, calm, equine in parade situations are demonstrating adaptability and intelligence as they overide their natural instincts for suspicion and flight.

Dumb, you say? They react that way because they are dumb!? WRONG. Their natural reaction to the situations I have described is flight. But, with good training and experience they can come to understand what is an appropriate, safe, quick response. They can learn to deal with these situations because they are intelligent. Whether it be as a police or carriage horse in the city or as a show horse in an arena - we have seen how incredibly adaptable and intelligent these magnificent animals can be.

Back to their hearing: Each individual horse's hearing is potentially either extremely acute or dull. Sounds like a contradiction, but it's not. Obviously, there is a wide variety of functional capability from one animal to another. As in people - some hear poorly, others well, and still others exceptionally well. When we speak of the horses inherently acute hearing we are speaking with some generality. I mentioned the "radar dish" like nature of the horses ears and told you of their ability to rotate in unison or separately. Whether riding or driving horses, one becomes accustomed to paying attention to the position of the ears. Both bolt-upright forward and alert almost as if pointing towards sound; both back, in relaxed alert unison, and obviously attentive to what sounds are behind; and at times with one ear forward and one back, allowing that they listen and discern two sources at once.

Kristi talks to this foal as it listens to her and to the photographer. Notice how the ears are aimed at the two sources of sound. The eyes tell us the foal feels no threat.

Much time and attention devoted to horses will show you that some individuals will "focus" on a sound (possibly with a sight) with such riveting attention that they exclude all others. It is as if they can't hear anything else for that moment. This is indicative of young horses or those of lesser intelligence, both of which may be more prone to repeated bouts of panic and confusion. Most of these horses can be trained to pay more relaxed general attention to their entire environment, as we explain later.

I enjoy riding in the pine forests on my old mare Rosie. Watching her ears and the slight movements of her head tell me the whereabouts of deer and other animals. "Reading" her ears I can tell if she recognizes (and excuses) the sound's source, what direction it came from and if it is near or far. After 10 years of working cattle together this has gone from my reading her body language to an actual dialogue.

It started with my patting her neck and saying things like "What's

39

that noise, girl?" or "It's okay, it's only a porcupine."

Over time I began to realize that Rosie could discern between my reassurances and my questions. Then one day I had a very important experience. We were riding in the woods, following my wife Kristi and her mare, and turning to the left. Out of the corner of my eye I caught something moving and turned my head right whispering, "What on earth is that?" Instantly Rosie's head came round to the right and she pivoted to stand facing the direction of the now disappeared mystery. She remained, ears ahead, face forward with a slight movement to the right as though following something, then she turned her head, looked at me, nudged my stirruped foot and pivoted back to the left to catch up with the others. At no point did I give her a customary signal to stop or turn. She had heard my whisper, read my concern, turned to measure the source, recognized it, excused it, told me everything was okay, turned and continued down the trail. Sound only plays a part in this story which also demonstrates what is possible from a long standing relationship based on mutual acceptance and trust.

The Miller stallion, Abe, paying real close attention. Note the position of the ears and how the one eye alone has us in focus.

As acute as the horse's hearing is, many is the time I had to "wake up" a good horse or team because they were day-dreaming and had turned their hearing off. Better you should discover this and wake "your children" than to have them surprised and startled by something which might cause them to react dangerously. The day-dreaming horse is a hazard to himself, in some situations, and being able to recognize the symptoms by reading the position of the head and ears is critically important. The sloppy, floppying ears are a sure sign, but learn to tell those from the stiff downturned ears of the ill horse.

While on the subject of the horse's hearing; I have spent over 20 years driving horses and 10 of those trying to share with folks some of what I've seen. Countless times I witnessed the dramatic changes that come over well-broke horses when the novice picks up the lines and talks to them. I can whisper to my horses and they will stop. The same horses will pretend to be hard of hearing with the novice. A regular lesson is for the beginner to learn to say "Whoa" in a firm stout tone rather than as a question or a whimper. But volume isn't the answer. The character of intent and expectation that the voice carries - that is the answer. I am not, however, suggesting that you need a tough tone or a threatening one. Your tone, whatever it is, needs initially to be understood and accepted as command.

With time your tone may change, but the outcome, if you are successful, will remain the same, willing acceptance.

I remember in 1973 watching old, frail Norm Stewart of Washington driving a big, young team of pulling horses into the ring at Monroe, Washington. I was photographing the pull and though less than 10 feet away could not hear Norm's verbal commands well enough to make them out. The horses could though, even over the roar of the crowd and worked on a soft line to perfection.

Understanding the character of the horse's hearing is important to succeeding as a trusted teamster.

This Amish buggy horse, at Topeka, Indiana Draft horse sale parking lot is listening, looking and probably smelling.

Sight

I hope I shall be forgiven in taking great metaphorical liberties while trying to describe for you the marvelous and contradictory system of sight for the horse. Certainly understanding how it works will help us to go a long ways towards forgiving this wonderful creature while marveling at its resourcefulness. This does not pretend to be a scientific discussion but it is accurate in descriptive outline.

Humans have a single lens to each eye. And that lens, when working properly, has the capacity to expand and contract quickly accomplishing two things simultaneously. One is to allow more or less light into the eye. And the other is to focus on the image seen.

The horse eye's entire exposed surface is covered by convexities (or slight bulges), each of which is a lens of different strength. Commonly those "lenses" on the bottom half of the horse's eye appear to serve distance vision while those at the top are for close-up. In the center of the eye is a lens with a very slow moving capacity to contract. Add to this that they have semi-lateral vision (eyes to the side of the head) and that they are color blind.

These physiognomy result in phenomenon and patterns we might all recognize and now better understand. For example, with semi-lateral vision the horse is blind up near its forehead, yet able to see flies on its hocks while facing straight ahead.

41

Have you ever picked up on how a horse will notice something faraway, raising its head with slow side-to-side movements, until finding focus? For any long distance the horse will look out of the bottom third of the eye. The side-to-side motions are a selection process as the animal looks to find the right "lens" to focus with. And some measure of "judgement" must enter in because it is the individual horse which chooses the correct focus. An animal incapable of any judgement might accept a fuzzy or double image before going through all options twice in order to select the correct one. Exercising choice is, once again, a hallmark of intelligence.

Notice the position of this filly's head as she struggles to see clearly that which it suspects.

Another example; notice how the horse positions its head when coming upon something closeup and confusing - like a puddle of water in the road.

The natural reaction is to lower the head and find a lens on the top of the eye which will give clear focus. If very close the horse will have to back up some. (The snorting you may hear is a natural nervous warning to whoever or whatever the boogey man might be.) Once focus is found the horse may slowly approach until smell and/or touch can be called in to help. If however the horse's natural process of focus and discovery is interrupted, the horse, with instincts unchecked, will try to run away. Remember flight or escape is a natural defense mechanism of the horse.

But also remember that the equine capacity for understanding, acceptance and intelligence is great. Simply put:

GIVE THE HORSE THE SAFE OPPORTUNITY TO "KNOW" and "ACCEPT" THE THREAT and it will no longer need or want to run away.

Or...

With horses, acceptance changes the character of reaction.

For so many people the great frustration with horses is the difficulty and general bother of having to "deal with" the shieing or jumpy horse. Whether as a work horse or saddle horse, in town or on the farm, the horse that jumps out of its socks each time it notices something new and strange will "bother" you if you let it. And the condition IS aggravated by how we react. But before getting into how we contribute to the problem, let's look again at WHY it happens in the first place and how sight figures in.

A. The horse's natural first mechanism of defense is flight.

B. Given the opportunity to understand the character of most "hazards" most horses will quickly accept it and forget flight.

C. Hearing and smell in horses is so acute and reliable that these senses (along with touch) can bring reassurance much faster than information gathered from sight.

D. Vision in horses is impaired if only in terms of response time. If the horse is not allowed adequate time to "find focus" and to understand the identity of a hazard it will take flight (run away).

E. Because of the limitations of horse's eyesight, when thrust upon an unknown and frightening object (or in some cases circumstance), the confusion is aggravated by the image being double, or fuzzy or larger than actual. The reaction is to jump back into some "safer" zone and figure out the hazard, focus on it. The horse knows his other senses are more quickly or instantly reliable. When

Flight is the horse's first line of defense in the natural world.

the eyesight sends confusing information the horse says to himself - let's back up and figure this out - he's not saying, at the first, "let me out of here!" That comes later and only if he's assured the threat is genuine or he is unable to access the threat.

So the "shieing" of the horse from some "seen" but "unrealized" or "confusing" object or phenomenon is the animals' first effort to understand the problem.

Training can alter this initial physical reaction into something that is less of a hazard to the person who is with the horse.

But before suggesting how training might do that, let's back up and look at those obvious ways we contribute to the problem.

As we said, when the horse shies from some confusing visual surprise he's backing up and working to focus his eyesight and employ all of his senses to figure out if this thing he sees (a piece of plastic flapping in the wind) is a genuine threat to his safety. He is calling on all of his natural, feral instincts to help him make an intelligent decision about self-preservation. Should he get away from the "thing" right now? Or is it a harmless object?

When that horse jumps back, its adrenalin starts pumping. Its skin becomes an ultrasensitive radar system. Its properties of extra-sensory perception become heightened. Taste, smell and hearing all work in an accelerated mode. And eyesight tries to help. In that state of being the horse is highly receptive, highly impressionable.

Enter us.

If we share this moment with the horse we contribute to how the animal handles it NO MATTER WHAT WE DO.

For example:

The horse shies and we;

a. become frightened ourselves by the jumping or backing animal. We try to figure out the problem with the horse, assuming its within the animal and not outside of it. Our fear is translated to either;

1. anger and impatience with the horse when we slap it, jerk it around, force it ahead, yell at it.

In which case the horse's confused state is aggravated because it's being denied the opportunity to understand the initial confusion. And the sensorial memory of this flapping piece of plastic now will include the added problematic dimension that this horse expects to be abused by the handler whenever he comes upon the same piece of plastic. Eventually the result might be to guarantee the horse will try to run away the very instant the object is sensed in order to avoid the whole unfortunate experience. That flight might include the need to lose the handler.

Or our fear is translated to;

2. resignation.

The situation is beyond us and we cannot deal with it except to back away and take the horse with us. Sometimes we feel as though we're protecting the horse, but in truth more often we're protecting ourselves. Removing the animal in that situation has the danger of assuring it that the object was indeed dangerous without the horse having had the opportunity to truly measure the identity and nature of the hazard. The horse picks up on our fear as further confirmation. Now whenever faced with the same stimuli the horse will be reminded that it left the scene last time and with good cause.

And in either case we, the handlers, have forfeited one of our best opportunities to build on a lasting relationship with the animal based on acceptance and trust.

That opportunity might be successfully handled this way:

The horse shies and we:

Make a quick assessment of any actual physical danger posed to us while we read the horse's ears and head position to determine the location of the "threat."

    Now we work to relax our own mind (think about something totally unrelated) and speak in calm, matter-of-fact tones asking and saying the obvious:

    "What is that thing?"

    "Oh, I see, it's a piece of plastic."

    "Is that bothering you?"

    "Well, take your time to focus on it."

    "When you're feeling a little reassured we'll go up a little closer and see if it smells."

    You do not want to talk loud, sound nervous, or slip into phony assurances like:

    "It's okay, boy. It won't bite you."

    I'm not suggesting that the horse knows what you're saying linguistically. It does, however, read your tone of voice and the character of what you're saying. If you are casual and matter-of-fact and appearing to be disregarding this "object," the horse will add that information to the process of trying to focus. When you slip into phony, protective assurances the frightened horse - just like the frightened person - picks up that what you're trying to say is that IT IS A DANGER but be brave. The horse just reads IT IS A DANGER. Instead, however, if your posture is an unfazed "it's no big deal" coupled with the patience to allow the horse ALL the time it needs to assess the hazard you have WON a very big prize. Because over time the horse will come to trust your part in the process and literally learn that if the particular surprise of the moment doesn't bother you he won't let it bother him.

    This is a simplified example of how the limitations of the animals' eyesight, coupled with the horses natural intelligence, can be used to build the best possible relationship.

    One final note on the eyes as portals: I have noticed when working with nervous, apprehensive, green horses that they become proportionately more nervous if I insist on sustained direct eye contact. I do not know why this is but it does happen in almost every case with but three catagorical exceptions: 1.) the sick horse, 2.) the dominate mature stallion, 3.) a nursing mare seperated from her foal.

    I will cover this later in training discussions but experience has shown that avoiding

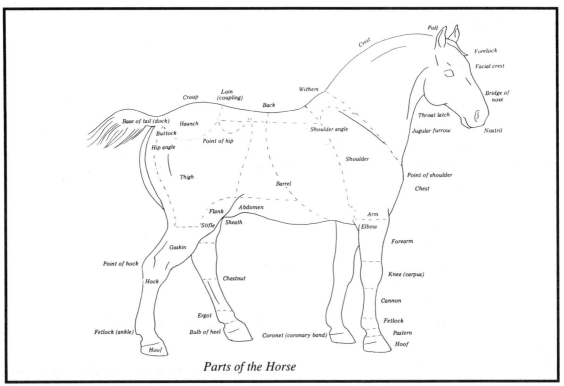

Parts of the Horse

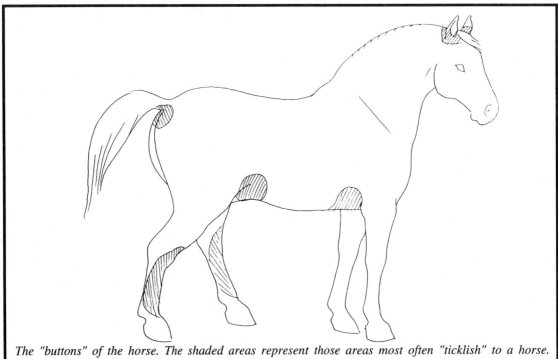

The "buttons" of the horse. The shaded areas represent those areas most often "ticklish" to a horse. Important information when desiring to measure a horse's temperament.

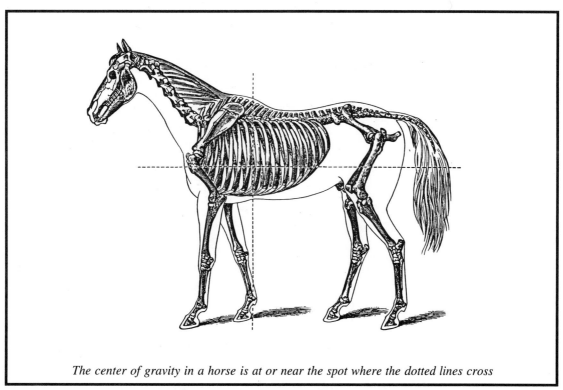

The center of gravity in a horse is at or near the spot where the dotted lines cross

The horse's base of support

sustained (the horse sees it as "threatening") eye contact is a training tool when working for total acceptance.

Touch

Remember seeing, in person, on TV, or in the movies, the teamster who will pick up the lines - whether to a carriage horse or a stage coach six-up - and slap the animal(s) hard while yelling "Heyah!" ? We've already established that horses have sensitive hearing. their sense of touch is every bit as acute. A single, tiny gnat, flitting around in hidden places, barely touching the ends of hairs, can drive the best horse buggy. Understanding this, especially after long relationships with horses, you'll come to realize how bizarre, brutal, silly and unnecessary it is to shake or slap the lines and holler at horses to make them go. (In fact many of today's 'slightly' trained horses would bolt and run with such a surprise.) Watch the best teamsters and you'll see exhibits of great subtlety and respect when they pickup the lines and speak to their horses. Those times when a horse needs to be tapped with a line, and there are some, will be spoken of later.

Jess Ross scratches Queenie under the belly band and she gives a clear indication of her pleasure.

Horses are able to read many things through touch that humans have difficulty with. We can share with horses similar conclusions from similar sensations but because of our odd cultural upbringing in these areas we are disinclined and embarrassed by them.

Watch horses meet each other in the open. The head is perpendicular to the ground, neck bowed and head's askance, not facing straight ahead. (This is for vision. Remember top of the eye for closeup focus.) And they must move their heads slightly to the side because of their semi-lateral (eyes to the side of the head) vision.

The first thing to touch is air, as they breathe into each other's nostrils measuring the scent in their memory bank. Their noses then might touch. If they are unfamiliar with each other, at this point one or both will squeal a warning and strike the ground with a front foot. If they accept one another they will often step ahead and simultaneously touch the side of the head to neck (as though necking). This might last for just a second or it might result in a back scratching session. (Imagine going through this routine with the next person you meet?)

As much as any recognition of the odors, a horse gets reassurance from the feel of any animal's breath and a reading of the touch. By the same token, the frightened horse whose systems are all on alarm can be sent into a fleeing panic by the slightest unforewarned or unfamiliar touch.

The horse's great sensitvity to touch can come into play within training also. Of course we will go into this at greater length further into the text but let me mention here that tremendous strides are made by getting the "new" animal accustomed to the widest variety of things touching him repeatedly and in a totally safe environment. In some circles this is called "sacking out" and refers to the practise of touching a partially restrained horse all over its body with a feed sack or cloth, doing this repeatedly until the horse "learns" to accept it. "Sacking out" has evolved to mean many different things which are intended to accomplish the same end. But all of them address the same recognition of the horse's heightened sense of touch and the need to, through that portal, gain full acceptance. The horse in harness must early on, be helped to learn that things hanging on it, varying pressures from straps, collar, chains, etc, lines flipping over a back, almost anything touching or landing on him is NOT a threat. Given this you might begin to understand how absurd it is then to use the slap of the lines and a yell to "frighten" your animals to go. It is the very opposite of the sort of relationship you want and certainly denies much of what is possible.

Judson Schrick's Belgians waiting for the plow on their Iowa farm.

You can learn to speak softly to your horse and "expect" that they will respond with the appropriate, desired, response.

The equine in harness and hitched is a motive power source which, with the keenest sensitivity and intelligence on your part, can develop more forward gears, smoother gear changes, differing braking speeds, improved turning radius and overall better fluidity with every shared working moment.

And for the long haul, as a teamster you'll find the most important aspect of "touch" comes into play with the horse's mouth and how we make it work with a bit and line pressure.

All of what has been said and suggested to this point comes into critical focus in this relationship of the horse's mouth to your hands.

Try a little empathy. Imagine you have a steel bar inserted into your mouth and held in place and that straps run back behind you to some unseen handler. It's easy to figure out that a confusing routine of pulls and slaps accompanied by yelling in a unknown language would create a nightmare for you.

Turn this picture around and imagine the slightest pressure on the lines, and always done in a consistent design to "help" you understand what is desired.

There is a saying, "good hands make the teamster", and it's certainly true. That is not to deny the human brain, it's to say that within the character of the touch and restraint you take to the animal, through your hands, lies much of the potential you have as a teamster. And this is true because the equine, through its heightened sense of touch, is reading your nature as well as your signals. Gaining that important acceptance we speak of comes in large part from the nature of your touch and the quality of their touch.

50

Taste

We have ways of knowing that the equine sense of taste is also quite acute. Differences of the slightest nature in drinking water or hay might "worry" an animal enough to have them refuse to eat or drink.

In the day of Britain's secret teamster societies clever tricks were frequently pulled to give the illusion of some black mastery over horses. These tricks often employed a working knowledge of the horse's sense of taste as well as smell.

Possibly within the catagory of taste should come some mention of one of the horse's great weaknesses. Grains and sweet-feeds in a domesticated environment can easily become a narcotic to the horse. For the horses some fears are temporarily forgotten, some normal cautions are set aside. Most intelligence becomes chaff in the wind when the initiated horse is offered grain. It would seem that the horse has become a manipulated "junkie". Yet, there is a more telling "other" side to this. There are tens of thousands of horses that cannot be caught without first being offered grain as an inducement, and this is, in my estimation, proof positive that these horses have demonstrated they can outsmart some of "we" mere humans. They have "trained" us to this prerequisite. It is comic but it is also dangerous. The well-trained accepting equine WILL come when called without reward of grain and gladly accept the offered halter. Anything less than this is an indication that the training is dangerously inadequate. Much more on this in later sections.

"Benjamin Franklin" begging for a reward.

Within this text you will find repeated references to the relationship between the horse's mouth and the teamster's hands. Putting a polish on a

51

finely tuned, carefully developed connection with a horse can at times prove to be a balancing act, juggling broken rules with compassion and rigidity. For example, understanding the horse's penchant for sweets, one clever trick for training a ready and willing acceptance of the bit and headstall is to coat the mouthpiece with a little molasses. The hazard, of course, is that the animal will expect the molasses and give difficulties in its absense. So, if the rule is to avoid sweet food rewards and the goal is to win acceptance to a challenging circumstance, the use of the sweet should be a solitary inducement (as trickery) used only by someone who understands the hazard and the goal (and enjoys the sometimes paradox of the effectiveness of contradiction).

Returning to the example of bitting a horse; the realization that taste may be an ally should perhaps be turned around to a view of taste and touch in the mouth as possible problem areas. Comfort of the horse, in this case, with specific regard to the head and mouth will include taste. In a training situation where the animal is new to receiving a bit, taste/comfort become critical factors. Remember that it is our challenge to understand the degrees to which we are training the horse with everything we do (or don't do) care must be taken that the taste, temperature and "feel" of that first bit are all neutralized. If the first time a bit is introduced it has a strong

Don eats as he does his share of pulling this Ontario grain binder driven by John Male.

unpleasant chemical taste from some solvent or metal polish and/or rough cutting edges and/or is extremely cold to the touch these conditions will cause the animal to try to refuse the bit. Worse yet this experience will have implanted a negative experience with the horse. The horse will probably attempt to refuse the bit next time. You will have begun a process of "training" the horse to be difficult to bit. If however, care is taken to have a clean, smooth, warm comfortable bit inserted quickly and casually - in a matter-of-fact way - the best beginning will be had without gimmick or inducement.

In cold weather care must be taken not to put a frozen steel bit into the horse's mouth.

Although taste figures least into that realm of those equine senses which we will depend on for successful training, it, nonetheless, is a sense which can help teach us what sort of creature it is we are dealing with and perhaps depending on.

With hearing, smell and touch God has given the horse large hyper-sensitive areas to collect sensory data. With hearing the large radar outer ears coupled with equally large inner chambers collect sounds with great efficiency and accuracy. With smell, once again the large nostrils and nasal passages provide more than ample surface area for the collection and discernment of odor. In the case of touch, of course, it is the entire surface of the large animal which comes into play. Now, with taste, we have an enormous tongue and oral cavity to hone in on tastes. All together, with the notable exception of sight, it might be said that the equine's sensorial design is superior to that of humans at least for the job of reading, measuring and reacting to a changing external environment. Whereas we may have a superior natural capacity for reflection and abstract thought we have not demonstrated, as a whole species, much practical application of this capacity. In other words, horses as a rule are "quick to comprehend" and people are in general slow or dead to comprehension.

In the natural order of survival, quick accurate comprehension of external stimuli can save a horse's life. Taste, as well as the other four primary senses, feed the equine brain which makes determinations based in large part on past experience or lack thereof. If the taste or smell is associated with some harmful or unpleasant past experience a determination for reaction is swift and certain. However, if the sensory data registers "unknown" the

53

equine may struggle to make assessment. If no accurate determination can be made the equine will - unless an aggressive protective stallion - usually elect to put as much distance as possible between it and the unknown.

When the horse, however, is removed from a wild environment interesting changes may occur. Depending on the natural intelligence of the individual equine (yes, it does vary) and given an environment which couples security with behavioral boundaries (training) the intelligent (comprehending) human may witness amazing demonstrations of adaptability, curiousity, acceptance, rejection, comprehension and intellect. Horses have been known to teach themselves how to open complex gate latches with their lips! Horses have been known to get past their natural fear of strong jets of water, as from irrigation sprinklers and move into them directing the pressure to points of itch, soreness, or pain for the obvious relief the spray provides! (see photo page 65) Just two of the sillier examples we might provide to lead into evidence of thought in horses and how that evidence points to the existance of another unchartered, some might say unspeakable, sense.

Thought and the Sixth Sense

This is certain to be the most controversial part of this book, more so than our insistance that horses are intelligent mammals or the notion that horses can be taught acceptance. I fully realize that inclusion of these ideas, observations and conclusions will result in some people rejecting, out-of-hand, the entire text. That is most unfortunate because there is much material contained in the balance of this work which comes of generations of success by several other horsemen. So I plead, if the following text disturbs you, please pass on it and find something else in this book you CAN use.

Hopefully our scattered examples, of how it might be shown that horses comprehend elements of their external environment and come to some understanding, have at least made a case for how we might measure equine behavior to our best ends.

Within the section, in this chapter, on HEARING I recounted an experience with my old saddle mare Rosie. In that particular instance the mare demonstrated, quite clearly, that she was first "sensing" or reading" my mind and second that she was taking for granted that I did likewise. I wondered, and worried, after a sound and movement in the near woods. She "read" my concern, directed all of her sensory faculties to the perception of the "element" in the woods - measured it to her satisfaction - and then through her manner and thoughts, offered her assurance that everything was okay.

You might reasonably say to this either;

"That is too farfetched, too bizarre."

or

""So, who's in charge? You or the mare?"

or

"Isn't it possible you are reading too much into this?"

or

"So what? Big deal. It doesn't have any real bearing on training."

To the first response I say it is more normal and reasonable and acceptable than much of the "regular" world of humans. I believe humans have a natural sixth sense which is, in many western cultures, denied and feared.

As to the second, third and fourth queries. I remain in charge determining where and how we progress and what is allowable. But after a working relationship in excess of 10 years she has shown me the value in not discounting her contributions. The challenge, for me, is to orchestrate our partnership to my goals without violating mutual trust and acceptance. This mare has a dominate, aggressive personality - she naturally wants to be in charge. She is the sort of horse that would be difficult for most people to train. She is relatively fearless. When she sees a snake she will go to it and stomp it dead. If she is surprised by a flapping bit of plastic or unknown object she becomes cold and calculating, even angry - instead of prone to flight.

But to continue - using Rosie as an example - I'd like to recount an experience.

Rosie and the Dueling Motorcycle

Rosie served as both saddle and buggy horse. On a carriage, in traffic, she never worried about oncoming vehicles or those passing from behind. Be they gravel trucks or sports cars she could care less. On one particular clear afternoon when we lived on a coastal farm, I had traveled with Rosie on the buggy some 3 miles down a paved road to visit neighbors. It was a winding road bordered by forest, pastures and high dense hedges of wild blackberries. When approaching the end of a curve that fed a short straight-away I heard a motorcycle before I saw it. It was to my way of thinking no cause for alarm. When the cyclist made the curve, and saw horse and buggy approaching from 100 yards distance he stopped. I suppose he was being polite and concerned that his Harley Davidson might spook the horse. So he sat still and very softly revved his engine to keep the motor from dying. He was waiting for me to pass. His single headlight was on and with each rev of the engine it would brighten. The overall effect, on me, was not unlike some bull pawing and snorting in preparation for a charge. But that was because I was trying too hard to guess as the mare's reading of the image. I could sense that Rosie's mood was tensing. I waved to the motorcyclist to come on by but he didn't seem to understand my signal. Now Rosie was stomping the pavement as she walked and she was snorting a warning to this odd dragonesque challenger. Because, by now, it was clear to her that this thing, who's one bright eye flared in unison with its own regular breathy snorts and puffs of smoke,

55

was indeed a challenger. I stopped the mare, stood up in the buggy and hollered at the cyclist to "come on by - damn it!". Rosie reared up in the shafts, angry and determined, I fell backwards and just then the now angry motocycle rider - who was only trying to be considerate in the first place - proceeded forward. I struggled to regain my place on the seat, my hands on the lines and my composure as Rosie - now firmly convinced something is wrong is prancing and darting from side-to-side. On our left was a ditch and barbwire fence, on the right was a blackberry hedge 8 foot high and 20 foot thick. She looked from one side to the other for a sensible way out. I was worried and got angrier. The cyclist scowled as he approached slowly in first gear. When he was within 30 feet I again hollered for him to just go on by. That did it, he got mad revved his engine and roared by, shifting into second as he passed. Rosie kicked at the buggy, reared up and leaped right into the blackberry bush and stood there with her ears flat back. My neighbor helped me get the mare and buggy out of the brambles. She was mad, mad at me, mad at the buggy and everything else. Instead of driving her straight home I took a roundabout trip of twice the distance until I was convinced she was over being mad.

This is a true story of something that happened to me driving an exceedingly well-trained, intelligent mare who knew me well.

I need to make some important distinctions before going into what I learned from the experience. At no time was there a threat that Rosie would "runaway", her move to the brush was an attempt to get out of the path of the challenger. After extricating ourselves from the brush she was as reliable as ever to drive with the single important exception that she was bullheaded when I forced her to pass the turn to our farm.

To understand my conclusions and lessons from this event imagine with me that you are the mare I've described in the situation of the story. This might be Rosie's point of view on what occured;

Long way before my human cohort has heard its approach I've made out the sound of the approaching motorized vehicle. Experience tells me that it will approach at a steady speed, keeping its place on the left side of the road. Plenty of experiences have reassured me that this is the case. There it is coming around the corner - but it's stopping?...it's blocking our way?...it's making threatening noises and winking its' big bright solitary eye! Big deal, it can't block our way, it's just some mechanical vehicle, we've seen lots of those. So get out of the road, or at least move over! I'll snort and stomp and show it I'm not afraid. Now what's that? I'm getting this strong sense, this reading, that my human is upset, worried, angry. What does he know that I don't? Now I can smell the smoke from the engine. Now my human is yelling, really upset, terribly worried, maybe scared! This is nonsense, I don't like this, something is definitely wrong. Now here it comes. Okay, stay on your side! Maybe there's some way to get some space between us, no not into the ditch, no not into the bushes... There he goes again, my human has flipped his lid, can't much count on him. Whoa! here it comes - get out of the way! Ouch, into the berry bushes. Well. that was all very stupid and unnecessary.

I think it's time we just went home...

Well, I've taken great risk with this exercise in imagination but I hope its worth the silly effort. Because the points I want to make are so important. Most of the problems we have with horses come from our refusal to grant them understanding and accept that we often are the problem. I'm not sure, given the particulars of the motorcycle story how it might have turned out different but I do know now that I aggravated a difficult and unique situation with my actions and thoughts. Rosie and most horses I've known can "read" my mind. Maybe not specifics but certainly moods and generalities. In that cycle situation, if I had ignored the vehicle and offered casual reassurance to Rosie we might have driven right on by with no more than a stiff neck and a snort. I know that I cannot fault her in her actions, she was working with what stimulus and memory she had to understand the situation and deal with it properly and safely. Had she previous successful or unsuccessful experience with a dueling motorcycle she could be expected to behave accordingly. As an important footnote: She being of a dominate nature it was critically important not to allow her to determine the course of action immediately following the incident. It was THE time to reinforce firm yet casual control. In this way some measure of my inadequacy during the event was thinned. (It was almost as if the boogey-man jumped us and she expected me to defend her only to find that I went to pieces. Extreme analogy perhaps but the feelings fit.)

Horses read our minds, they have a telepathic capacity which we can only guess the full nature of. But it does exist, you see and feel evidence of it repeatedly, (unless of course you refuse to). Stand behind a team of horses which are wearing blinders and concentrate on one of them - stare at the back of that horse's head. And watch its reaction. In a short time this horse will move its head and ears to try to figure out who or what it feels.

Bud and Dick to the Rescue

My first experience with this occurred in 1975 when plowing with geldings Bud and Dick. My friend, Ray Drongesen, had loaned me his Oliver contest sulky plow. He had modified a 2 way plow, removing one bottom and securing the hitch. This resulted in a riding plow with just two wheels, set directly opposite one another, which allowed a greated possibility of a clean straight handling of dead furrows. I was plowing up 10 acres for market vegetables and practicing for a plowing match. When Ray loaned me the plow he said,

"Pull that seat off and replace it. I put that big washer on there because there was a lot of rust and some cracking around the hole in the center of the seat. And take that coulter wheel off and sharpen it. It will make the plow pull easier."

Well, I shook the seat and it seemed solid enough so I just sharpened the coulter. And boy did I do a good job, it was like a razor.

57

Bud and Dick, Shire / Percheron cross geldings, had done a lot of plowing for me. We had an excellent working relationship. We were finally getting down to the dead furrows, this is where two sections (or lands) of plowed ground meet. Finishing up means turning over that last narrow strip of unplowed ground. To do this with a riding plow means that wheels will be running atop plowed ground. It can create a rough ride and a real challenge to the plow man. In order to keep the plow working properly it is important to maintain the proper depth and to control the overall level of the bottom of the moldboard.

Ray's contest plow was superior to most other sulkies because it had a straight across axle and 2 fully adjustable wheels. Most sulky plows have three wheels, one working behind in the furrow and two offset across from the moldboard. With Ray's plow it was possible to work the adjusting upright handles to compensate for irregularity in the wheel paths and thereby maintain a straight and level plow share. And that translated to the best chance to get that last standing strip of unplowed ground cut and turned. This was a challenge I enjoyed, it seemed to climax a piece of work and give some small testimony to the care and effort the horsefarmer puts into his calling.

But in order to do this piece of precision adjustment, as the plow moved forward, I needed both hands free. I tied the lines and hung them over the top of one handle. Bud and Dick didn't need to be driven they knew right where to walk, so my hands were free to adjust the wheels as we plowed. And if I did need them the lines were within inches of my hands. It was all working beautiful except that the ups and downs of the adjusting wheels caused me to rock back and forth on the seat of the plow.

A third of the way down the 1/8 mile dead furrow the seat broke off! I felt it go and raised up on my feet and said "Whoa". The horses stopped immediately and I fell forward scurrying to avoid handles but grabbing for balance and muttering more "whoas". The end result found me with one leg under the tongue and wedged up against the front side of the sharpened coulter. The driving lines were up and out of my reach and twisted, as was I. I couldn't get myself free. The team stood quiet, resting and relaxed. I quickly assessed that should the team move ahead I would loose my leg at the thigh. I didn't want to say anything lest they misinterpret my signal, so I laid there thinking to myself, "If you do anything please back up...Please back up, please just back up."

I will never forget what happened next. Bud was the furrow horse and the definite leader, he raised his head and slowly bent his neck to look back down along the tongue and at my prone form. Dick followed suit. Then Bud turned and looked back down the outside and right at me. Straightening up, they then both took one step backwards, releasing the bite of the coulter, and stood perfectly still as I scrambled free.

A quick inspection, after hugging and kissing the team, showed that the complete center of the seat had broken out - like the torn open top of a tin can.

Did the horse's back up in response to my thinking it, willing it? Or did they back up

58

because it gave them some added comfort? There is certainly no way of knowing or proving it. But I don't care. What's important about this experience to me, is that it gave me the confidence to suspect horses are capable of some extra sensory perception. And to use that suspicion, over these last 20 years, to my great reward and comfort.

Bobbie in the Furrow

I share this last example with much hesitation because it is dangerously specific and I've witnessed the discomfort and disbelief it often causes in listeners.

I've owned Bobbie, a Belgian mare, longer than any other horse (17 years). She's 26 at the time of this writing and receiving special retirement care. I know I've enjoyed a unique and special relationship with this good big mare. She's plowed too many acres to count and always worked in the furrow.

After my experience with Bud and Dick I began to experiment with this ESP business in horses. And Bobbie proved to be my best subject.

In the late seventies I used Oliver riding plows with three abreast on the sulky and six up (3 + 3) on the gang plow. With the big hitch I always used Bobbie as the lead furrow horse.

When working on the sulky plow Bobbie had a habit of stepping up out of the furrow whenever we stopped to rest. She never moved the plow, she just seemed to want her big feet out of the furrow to rest. In the beginning I figured this was wrong and kept forcing her back in the furrow but with time I learned to accept that no harm was done and she was easy and willing to get back in the furrow to start the plow.

When we graduated to the 2 bottom gang and Bobbie moved to the lead an interesting little problem developed. When stopping to rest Bobbie would step up onto the land as before. So when it came time to start up the plow again I'd speak to Bobbie and the rest of the hitch figured it was time to go. This lead me to try to devise a way to get Bobbie into the furrow, prepatory to starting the whole hitch, but without saying a word.

It was pretty spooky. It worked from the first time and every time after. I would stare at Bobbie, concentrate on her and think, repeatedly, the simple message (visualizing) "get in the furrow." And she would move her head as though listening and then carefully step sideways back into the furrow! And no words were spoken.

Occasionally this exercise would cause a little confusion on the part of another horse or two in the hitch but only once or twice. The most sensitive to outside interception of the cue were very young horses, very alert and anxious, and their only reaction was to look around as if after a sound.

But Bobbie always caught the cue and stepped back in the furrow.

These are the sorts of examples I would bring to the argument that horses possess a sixth sense. And there are many more such stories. My particular, and individual, acceptance of these experiences has gone towards the construction of a thoery about how the equine thinks.

Horses' perceive. Those perceptions are fed into a cognitive process which results in horses knowing. But that knowing does not result in a capacity for complex reasoning, for the formation of ideas, or for intellectual thought. Yet horses do have a uniquely specialized capacity for understanding which I believe stems from their inability to separate sensory perception and intuitive influences. All three of these enter the brain of the horse with equal force. And, as they join in the workings of the equine mind, have similar weight in the formulation of understanding and judgement. This mixture of the psychic and the concrete often results in behavior which we humans find thoughtless or irrational.

But that is only because we are somewhat incapable of appreciating the entire sphere of influence affecting the brain of the horse. If we could but understand how the horse thinks we could first learn how to train this splendid animal to work with us - and second learn how and when to allow the horse to contribute its unique intelligence to our partnership.

It is not a process of excusing the horse its natural limitations but rather appreciating its unique and marvelous mental workings.

Old Bobbie enjoying her retirement

Comparative Views of the Horse

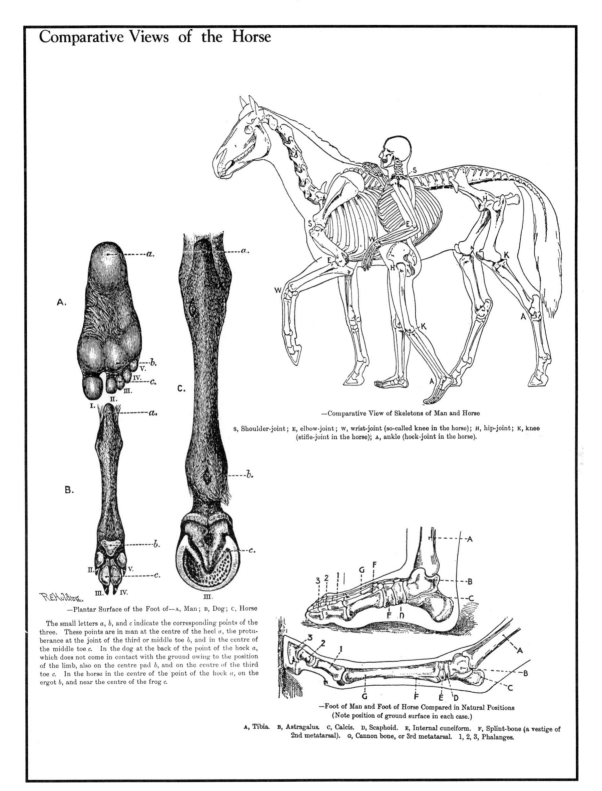

—Comparative View of Skeletons of Man and Horse

s, Shoulder-joint; E, elbow-joint; w, wrist-joint (so-called knee in the horse); H, hip-joint; K, knee (stifle-joint in the horse); A, ankle (hock-joint in the horse).

—Plantar Surface of the Foot of—A, Man; B, Dog; C, Horse

The small letters *a*, *b*, and *c* indicate the corresponding points of the three. These points are in man at the centre of the heel *a*, the protuberance at the joint of the third or middle toe *b*, and in the centre of the middle toe *c*. In the dog at the back of the point of the hock *a*, which does not come in contact with the ground owing to the position of the limb, also on the centre pad *b*, and on the centre of the third toe *c*. In the horse in the centre of the point of the hock *a*, on the ergot *b*, and near the centre of the frog *c*.

—Foot of Man and Foot of Horse Compared in Natural Positions
(Note position of ground surface in each case.)

A, Tibia. B, Astragalus. C, Calcis. D, Scaphoid. E, Internal cuneiform. F, Splint-bone (a vestige of 2nd metatarsal). G, Cannon bone, or 3rd metatarsal. 1, 2, 3, Phalanges.

Form of the Head and Behavioral Tendencies

Much has been written about the form of the individual horse's head and how it can tell us about the horse's natural behavioral tendencies. I have seen too many exceptions to the so-called rules to believe in them wholesale. In keeping with the core, inclusive, philosophy of this text, I offer my renditions of illustrations from a turn of the century training pamphlet as reference information or curiosity (your choice).

TEACHABLE, KIND, OBEDIENT

NERVOUS, TEACHABLE, RUNNER

Form of the Head and Behavioral Tendencies

STUBBORN, DULL,
BALKY

OUTLAW, BOLTER,
SNEAKY

The late Jack Bissel mowing hay at Singing Horse Ranch.

Stacking hay on Singing Horse

Chapter Three

Caring for Horses

Although this is a critical factor in good horsemanship we will not devote much space here to the specifics of care. Instead this will be a brief discussion of those aspects of care which can influence success in training. For more in-depth information of the care of horses we recommend *The Work Horse Handbook.*

Feeding

The horse has a very small stomach and massive sensitive intestinal tract. For these reasons you must be knowledgeable about what to feed and when. (See *Work Horse Handbook* charts.)

As with any living animal proper nutrition, or lack of it, can have an effect on the individual horses attentiveness and capacity for physical movement. You cannot expect the best results from an animal in training if that animal is perpetually hungry.

But equal care must be taken not to overfeed high energy feedstuffs if the only thing expected of the animal is attention. Hard physical labor burns off the energy provided by grains and concentrates. If there is no demand by the physiognomy of the individual horse for high energy feeds those carbohydrates can affect the disposition of the idle horse. Hypertension, nervousness and unruliness can result. It's not unlike what happens to a person on a high sugar diet and with nothing to do.

Parasite Control

Horses with high infestations of internal parasites are susceptible to a wide variety of serious health problems and physical symptoms. External parasites can create problems none the least of which might be

The author's gelding, Barney, is the world's only self-cleaning draft horse. Whenever he's in the proximity of a sprinkler he will move his body to direct the water flow wherever he wishes.

driving horses nuts. It may be difficult to get a green horses full attention if it is being hassled by flies.

The good teamster learns about parasites and devises a sensible, affordable way to control them. Get the assistance of a good veterinarian.

Lameness

The horse with sore hooves or leg joints, or any of a variety of lameness problems may be difficult to train especially if its attention is always with the soreness or pain. Lameness also adds further specific difficulties if it makes training to handle feet impossible. Get the assistance of a good farrier, one who understands the difference between a work horse foot and that of other specialty horses. Farriers as a rule do not wish to train your horse to allow it's feet to be picked up. Handling the feet, early on in training, is a very important part of building a good behavior in your animal. (See *Work Horse Handbook*.)

Reproductive Concerns

As you are about to learn, training depends in no small part on you being able to get and maintain the trainee's attention. Anything which intervenes with this is a possible

Stabling a Belgian on the Judson Schrick farm in Iowa.

problem. For this reason it is important to educate yourself with regard to the emotional changes which are directly tied to the reproductive realities of horses. For example; stallions in the vicinity of mares in heat cannot be expected to give full and undivided attention unless already conditioned to do so. The reverse is also true, mares in season, whether near stallions or not, may go through severe mood swings that can create training problems. Also mares which are nursing foals will not prove very attentive. A real nightmare example would be the mare in heat separated from her offspring and subjected to training while near a stallion.

That said, it's interesting to note that pregnant dry mares are often easier to train than open dry mares.

Educate yourself about the reproductive realities of mares and stallions before attempting training to understand or appreciate all the variables that might crop up.

Miscellaneous Ailments

If you insist on training a horse which is suffering from, or recovering from, a particular ailment it might be important to understand the symptoms. For example: Periodic ophthalmia, or moonblindness, is a chronic condition of the eye or eyes. It causes the horse to go blind in one or both eyes for a short period of time. Understanding this can help explain some strange doings during training.

It is impossible to list all the ailment variables here. I just want you to know that it can affect your work and that you need to educate yourself about the health of the animal you're working with.

Grooming

Working horses in harness can cause the animals to sweat and secrete body salts which mix with dust to form an uncomfortable crust on the horse's hide. You can imagine, I'm sure, how good it might feel to have this crust brushed off the back and legs. Beyond that the currying of the horses helps to keep the skin and hide healthy.

One famous northwestern teamster, Mel Anderson, swears by the grooming process to "teach the animals to like you."

Stabling

If you are keeping your trainee horses stabled attention should be paid to their comfort. General dimensions and structural concerns are presented in the **Work Horse Handbook.** While on these pages we offer a design of convertible double tie stall which works extremely well for us.

It should be noted that the horse that is held prisoner in an uncomfortable situation is less likely to make a willing work partner.

Convertible Double (Team) Tie Stall Design

CONVERTIBLE DOUBLE (TEAM) TIE STALL

MANGER

GRAIN & SALT BOX

DIVIDER POLE

TEN FEET WIDE

FLOOR SLOPES TO REAR, ONE INCH FALL IN EIGHT FEET.

By removing the pole, tieing up the chain, and hanging a gate from post to post, this stall can become an enclosed box affair. Care would need to be taken to prevent horses from going head-to-head or nose-to-nose at lower portions of dividing walls. If you anticipate using one or more of your doubles as part-time box-stalls, I recommend that you close off this portion. If you do this you should know that, in a fully closed barn, you have reduced the ventilation considerably and some allowance (i.e. a fan) must be made.

Pasture

If you are able to turn your trainees into a spacious corral pen or small pasture you will earn extra points and advantage. There is a direct relationship between the comfortable healthy horse and good, quick training results. Turning horses out for a period of time gives them freedom, opportunities to stretch and roll, and the added advantage of creating a rhythm of being haltered and brought to the barn for feed and grooming. This creates a willingness to be caught and handled. In this way pasture is a training tool. (A side word of caution; if you are working horses which are shod, perhaps with cleats or caulks, you must use your best judgement to determine whether or not the animals "sharing" the pasture will fight and kick. Otherwise you might come to that pasture in the morning and find a lame or injured work horse. If the horses are in training I recommend that they be barefoot.)

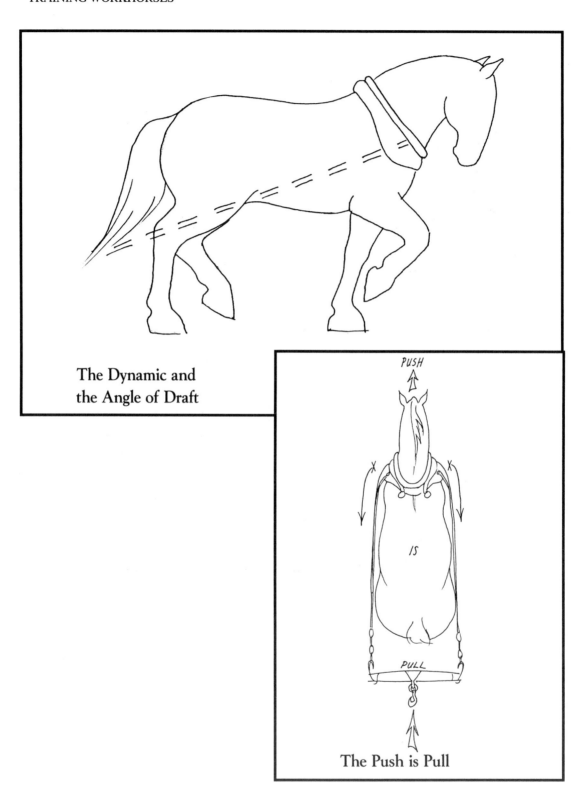

The Dynamic and
the Angle of Draft

PUSH

IS

PULL

The Push is Pull

Chapter Four

How Horses Work

Dynamics, Harness, Bits, Harnessing

This is a short illustrated discussion of the shape and structure of the horse relative to the work he is expected to perform, and a look at the mechanics of the harness employed in that work. For a greater depth of explanation please see the **Work Horse Handbook** and discussions in the **Training Teamsters** section of this volume.

Dynamics of Pulling

The physical structure of the horse is a composite of a mass of "links," bones, joints, muscles, tendons and ligaments working together to accomplish even the simplest of movements. In the working portion of the horse, potential strength can often be measured in direct relationship to the weakest part of the individual system. As illustrated on the previous page, through the proper fit and alignment of collar and tugs the horse translates a pushing action into a pulling action. PUSH IS PULL; that's the mechanics of draft. Whether it be with a collar or a breast strap harness. The horse's shoulders (or chest) push against an assembly which transfers this into a pulling action with the tugs or traces. Obviously, questions of pulling efficiency can be greatly affected by proper fit of harness just as much as by the specific conformation of the working horse.

Harness

In order to take maximum advantage of the horse's inherent capacity for draft (or pulling) man, for centuries, has redesigned rigging that would fasten to the animal and work as a pulling mechanism. The differing specific purposes of this rigging include:

First - to hang, fasten, and/or balance (otherwise anchor) ropes, chains or leather straps onto the individual horse. And that these would function as the structure to pull with from a point on the shoulder of the animal.

Second - to outfit the horse's head and mouth in such a manner that a person would have a guidance system between him and the animal.

Third - to provide geometric systems of interlocking "lines" that allow two or more horses to be "guided" in unison.

Fourth - if using a wheeled vehicle, to provide some manner in which the vehicle could be backed.

In this text we will disregard all of the rich array of harness variations, past and present, and limit ourselves to a discussion of modern-day western-type harness. This is not an endorsement of one style or design over others. It is an attempt to simplify the discussion to aid in the understanding of how and why harness works, all with a goal of assisting people unfamiliar with work horses but insistent on training attempts.

Once again we must recommend that the novice spend some time with the ***Work Horse Handbook*** for a more indepth look at harness.

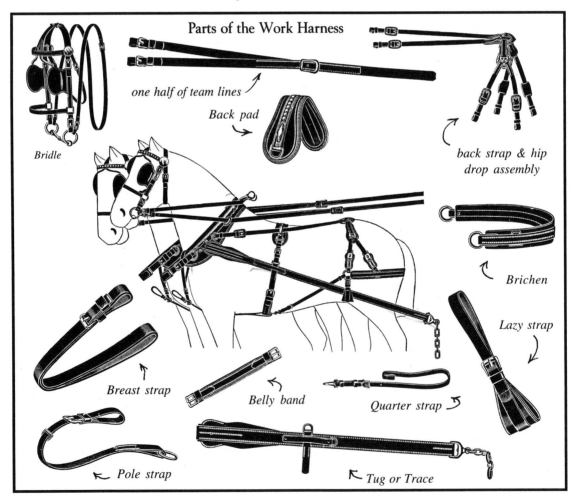

Parts of the Work Harness

Bridle

one half of team lines

Back pad

back strap & hip drop assembly

Brichen

Lazy strap

Breast strap

Belly band

Quarter strap

Pole strap

Tug or Trace

Variations in Work Harness

For the sake of simplicity we are only discussing a few designs and in no way endorsing these over others.

Plain western-style brichen farm harness.

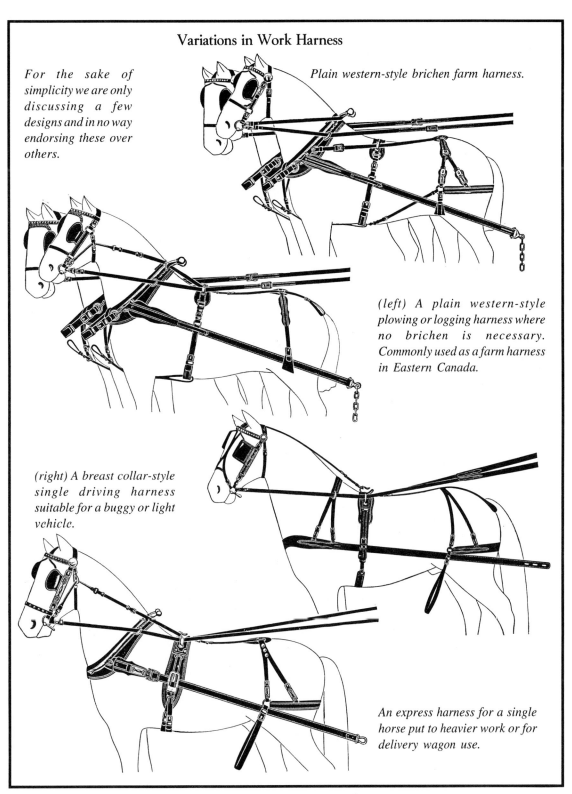

(left) A plain western-style plowing or logging harness where no brichen is necessary. Commonly used as a farm harness in Eastern Canada.

(right) A breast collar-style single driving harness suitable for a buggy or light vehicle.

An express harness for a single horse put to heavier work or for delivery wagon use.

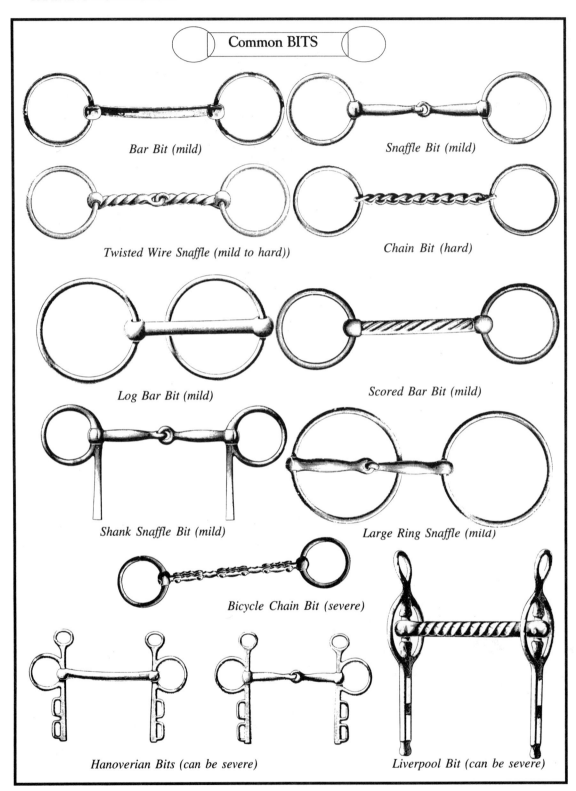

Common BITS

Bar Bit (mild)

Snaffle Bit (mild)

Twisted Wire Snaffle (mild to hard))

Chain Bit (hard)

Log Bar Bit (mild)

Scored Bar Bit (mild)

Shank Snaffle Bit (mild)

Large Ring Snaffle (mild)

Bicycle Chain Bit (severe)

Hanoverian Bits (can be severe)

Liverpool Bit (can be severe)

Old-time Training Bits

These bits were specifically designed for two purposes. Number one was to be used with hard-mouthed and/or runaway horses where extra leverage and pain could be inflicted. And number two to train the new horse to stop on command. In either case these bits were a disaster in the wrong hands and could be quite effective if used by a capable and experienced trainer. I do not recommend their use.

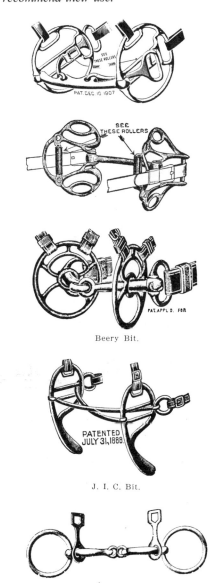

Beery Bit.

J. I. C. Bit.

Additional Harness Parts Identified

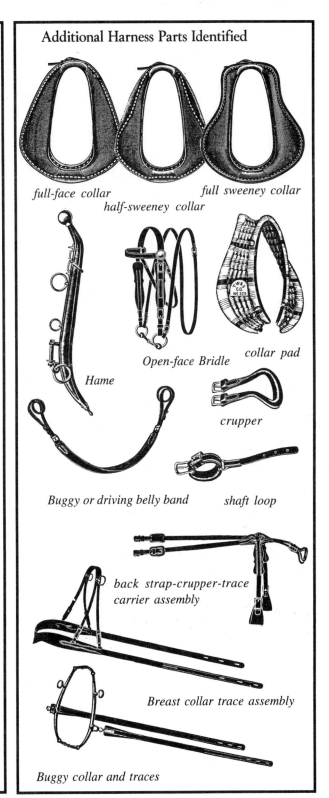

full-face collar

half-sweeney collar

full sweeney collar

Hame

Open-face Bridle

collar pad

crupper

Buggy or driving belly band

shaft loop

back strap-crupper-trace carrier assembly

Breast collar trace assembly

Buggy collar and traces

Bits and Bitting

There are thousands of designs of bits invented, through the ages, reflecting the humans ever-changing attitude about the best possible relationship and performance to be expected from (or with) the horse. We will only trouble ourselves with a handful of styles as they might relate to the training exercises outlined in this book. Other variations appear as integral to other notes within the broader training text.

It is my opinion that bits which combine an opportunity for gentleness with flex and comfort provide the teamster with the fullest range of communication through the hands to the animal's head and mouth. I have noted in the illustrations contained in this text those designs which are "mild". Certain corrective routines may justifiably call for a more severe bit, but in most cases it is my opinion that good training will remove the need for such measures. Please remember that we should have, as a goal, a driving relationship which requires only the subtlest variations in line pressure to result in desired activity. And this goal IS attainable.

Harnessing

The harnessing routine we have chosen to illustrate with photos is the one we employ during our training program.

In this case Jess Ross is harnessing "Thom" for the very first time. He's a coming four year old Belgian gelding that was originally "imprinted" as a day old foal. He was then handled regularly during his nursing weeks as his mother was part of the working string. He was castrated as a weanling and his feet were worked on by a farrier half a dozen times. He was put through the "acceptance training and roping out" routines immediately before this harnessing.

Here we are harnessing this horse in the round pen. You may be harnessing in a barn or other environs. Please be careful not to put yourself in a situation where you might get hurt. I recommend that you harness your horse(s) out in the open for the first few times. After you have a good working sense of what happens, or can happen, you'll be okay to harness in the tight confines of a stall. I regularly harness my horses in their tie stalls.

The photo captions will take you through the harnessing process. Please note: In the first five photos we demonstrate the proper fitting and fit of a collar.

First let your horse sniff and look at the collar. Open the collar at the top (if there is a pad, pull it to the outside as in this photo) and support both sides so that it does not fall open at the bottom and crack.

(Left) Slide the collar up onto the neck. (If you have one pull the pad over and under the collar.) Buckle, or fasten, the collar at the top.

(Right) Push the fastened collar against the neck and check to see if it fits properly. This collar does. There is just enough room at the throat to pass a hand in and the sides fit nicely.

(Lower Left) This photo demonstrates a collar that is too tight. You can see the fold of skin at the upper neck and it is so short at the throat that it would choke a horse which pushed against the collar. This is not good. If you want a horse to pull well you need to fit it with a proper collar. The fold at the top of the neck might suggest a thickset horse which requires a full-sweeney collar or a collar that is padded.

(Lower Right) This collar is much much too big. If you were to work a horse in a collar like this sores wouldn't definitely be the result.

(Right) We have the training harness hanging from two bent rods drapped over the round pen Juniper rails. On the left, the top hame strap hangs over the rod - on the right, one of the hip-drop straps is hung over the rod. Care is taken to hang the harness, hame strap first - then hip drop, the same way each time so that it is easy to pick up the harness without tangling. (Note in the background that we have several collars available to us to select from for proper fitting.)

A. *Because we are harnessing Thom for the first time and don't need any extra baggage, we have taken the bridle and lines off of the harness. Jess has passed his right arm under the brichen and hip-drop assembly...*

B. *....and continues to pass under the back pad...*

C. *...and reaches for the right-side hame with his right hand and takes the left side hame in his left hand.*

D. *Notice that he has taken hold mid-way in the length of the hame, this allows somewhat greater leverage to lift the portion of the harness and spread it open in preparation for the horse.*

E. *Jess has allowed Thom to view and sniff the harness before moving back, and into position, to lift the assembly over the collar.*

(In our training routine we ask the horse to stand untied, in the round pen and accept the harnessing. This is all part of a program of "best expectations". If we request, require, demand, and expect the best we feel we're always on the road to success.)

We don't "throw" the harness on the new horse.

If Thom had decided to walk away as we harnessed we would have simply stayed with him, calmly, until he stopped - usually as a response to our "WHOA".

78

F. Jess has set the hames in the collar groove and carefully balanced the bulk of the harness over Thom's back. This is done so that the harness doesn't slip, of its own weight, off the horse and startle him needlessly.

G. Jess moves to the front of the horse to sight in the placement of the hames. It is important that they are centered and properly positioned so that the trace point on the hames falls within the upper half of the "draft" or wide portion of the collar. Notice how the bulk of the harness is positioned on the back.

H. Now the bottom hame strap is coupled tightly. The top hame strap, and its fastening position on the top of the hames, is the main adjustment to get the hames to fit the collar properly. Hames come in different sizes with a 2 to 4 inch adjustment possible. The collar should fit the horse and the hames should fit the collar.

I. Jess has moved to the back and pulled the brichen down.

J. (right) Next comes the breast strap. In this harness a roller snap assembly connects the pole strap and breast strap into one piece.

79

L. The pole strap goes between the front legs and back to where the quarter straps snap into it.

K. A good view of the breast strap-pole strap assembly. The breast strap is snapped into place. The pole strap hangs straight down, awaiting hookup.

N. Pulling the tail out over the brichen.

M. Pulling the brichen assembly back.

O. (Left) Notice how accepting Thom is of this entire process, and he's not tied or restrained. This is the true beauty of the round pen "mutual acceptance" program.

P. (Above) Finally the belly band is fastened, loosely, and the only thing which remains is the bridling and stringing of lines.

Q. With your right hand spread the top of the bridle and pull up over the horse's head. Your left hand is available to put thumb and forefinger in the corners of the mouth if the horse resists the bridle.

R. Jess has drawn back the check rein and is snapping it into place. Thom has taken to this bridling process so well because of the "roping out" routine.

The harnessing is complete and Jess is checking the bit for proper fit. We don't want it so loose that the horse can get its tongue over. But neither do we want the bit so tight as to cause discomfort.

The single lines will pass through the top hame ring and fasten to the bit below where the check rein hooks in.

*For more in-depth discussion and some important variables to harnessing procedure we ask that you look to the **WORK HORSE HANDBOOK**.*

Five Belgians abreast on a two bottom pull-type plow near Millersburg, Ohio.

Chapter Five

What Can Be Expected?

You want to train horses and you need to know what you might reasonably expect of the finished product. And you want to know how long it will take. And you want to know the risks. And you want to know if you can do it.

What's A "Good Broke Horse?"

What's a "broke" horse? I mean "good broke", some may say "well broke", others may say "well trained", and others still might say "dependable". Pick your label, we all know what we're talking about, don't we? It all means the same, don't it? Perhaps not.

A "good broke" horse is one that does what you want it to, when you want it done. Right? A "good broke" horse is one that will stand there quietly while you harness or saddle it. And later, when you give it the command to go, it will, and at the speed you want. And when you want to turn or stop, this "good horse" does what you command without so much as a peep. I think not. I would like to suggest that this is a dangerously simplistic view of "well broke". A view that will most often result in a dull, slow, balky, lifeless animal with no interest in the working relationship.

Jess Ross mowing with his Percheron mares on Singing Horse Ranch. Photo by Sharon Ross

The frustration, in any discussion on this topic, is with the words. They get in the way. I don't want to get hung up on what "broke" means or the difference between it and "trained". What I want to do is help people understand, and communicate, what is possible, what is do-able, what might be reasonably expected of, and with, good horses. And the reason I want to do this is because the future of working horses and mules is with new

Gene and Bonnie Westberg of Baker City, Oregon.

Broke horses will do the job any where. Here John Male's team waits patiently for an equipment adjustment as folks look on in a small field right smack in the middle of a small Ontario, Canada, town.

people. And new people need to understand what they can expect so that they can set their goals. That is part of the reason why it is so important to me that we have the broadest understanding and agreement about what is a good work horse. With this comes a future, the best future.

What is a broke horse? What makes a broke horse? These two questions are closely tied to one another. The foundations, which have been laid in the early training of the animal, will determine not only the full depth of its potential trust-worthiness but also its ability to understand and enjoy the work. The horse, or mule, that has been approached and handled, from day one, as though it were a time bomb or an idiot, will be hard pressed to find room to "enjoy" or extend itself into the slave routine. Resistance or apathy will be the norm. On the other hand, the animal that is allowed the distance, respect and patience to understand the procedures asked of it, and given the opportunity to feel it is being "allowed" to choose the path of least resistance, this animal will display an eager supple pliancy and appetite for work that will continue to surprise even the most perceptive and optimistic teamsters. I am NOT suggesting that such an attitude and nature are only the result of certain training procedures. That is preposterous. What I am saying, or trying to, is that these favorable characteristics are part of the equine's nature. We can suppress them, and fight them, and work for subservience, solely. Or we can recognize them and use them to our own best advantage by "allowing" the opportunity for the horse to develop into a true working partner. The outcome of our training is more important than superficially measured results. When we are "done" with training (I prefer to believe we are NEVER done) we can proceed to marshall the animal through a routine to prove it's learned subservience. Or we can recognize the animal's understanding of harness, procedure, and signals, and enter into a lifetime adventure of fascinating working partnership, always open to the possibilities.

I hazard to jump into a lengthy discussion about broke horses

84

because I am convinced that the only way you can succeed in training them is if you, first, have a genuine interest in learning what makes horses tick. And second you have a clear understanding of what you want to accomplish. With that, the next thing you need is a well cultivated skill for observation. And last, but far from least, you must have a well honed ability to handle, and communicate with, the trained horse. (What value is the trained animal if the "operator" is unable to communicate what he or she wants?) These four elements are more important than any gimmicks, plans, systems or routines. Again, these four elements are:

     1. the desire to learn about what makes horses tick;

     2. knowing what you want to accomplish;

     3. a cultivated skill for observation;

     4. the ability to communicate.

The hazard comes into the picture because these four elements are so difficult to teach, illustrate, or communicate. How do you teach the desire to learn something specific? How do you help someone define their goals? How do you communicate an understanding of the skill of observation and its value? How would you illustrate, convincingly, the means to communicate with horses? These may be big reasons why we go for short cuts, and insist on simple procedures and devices, when training and working horses and mules in harness. The thrust of this argument is that short cuts give you short results. And that patience, common sense and persistence will give you long results, in other words "good broke horses".

Jess and Sharon Ross with their Percheron mares and fillies on parade.

But there is more, much more. There are aspects to this business that go beyond simple, quiet, obedience. You can rightfully expect an honest, trusting relationship with an intelligent, well-trained, experienced work horse to add capacities and capabilities to the working unit. Good, willing workers will provide you with extra muscle energy when the going gets tough. Good, trusting, understood horses will provide you with extra eyes, ears, noses, complete sensory systems, which are available to you if you are open to the messages. Team work. The teamster is part of that team work package.

I'm speaking here, primarily, of work horses in harness (as differentiated from pleasure or competition). I am not separating draft from saddle or pony. The important distinction is that the animal(s) "works" in harness. And that IS an important distinction because it provides a unique environ-

Young Mr. Schrick hooks three Belgians to the sulky plow on their farm in Iowa. The more you work them the easier it gets and wider the trust becomes. Yes, you can have horses that will stand quietly and patiently for you as you do the work of farm implement adjustment and hitching.

ment for the animal(s) that may (and often does) contribute critical factors to their behavior as well as yours. If you NEED to get a job done, a road traveled, a procedure completed with horses or mules, your attitude and expectations will be demonstrably, and critically, different from that which occurs when you're casual and less structured because recreation is the goal. Now add to the "NEED to get the job done" the possibility that it will take a lot of work and a lot of time. Hour after hour, day after day, week after week, that must be spent plowing that field, mowing that hay, traveling that road all while depending on those animals. Things happen. You change. The animals change. Your expectations will change and so will theirs. You will quickly learn that your overall efficiency is dramatically affected by your powers of observation and the care you take with overall husbandry and maintenance. And (this you may find hard to accept) the horse quickly learns the extent to which you pay attention and provide good care and maintenance. The horse learns that you often forget to provide water, or that feeding is sporadic and irregular, or that you take special care and attention with grooming and harness fit. If you regularly mess up, the

L.R. Miller takes Barney and Molly into a pond to clean out weeds. Trusting horses will go where you ask.

horse or mule will develop a grudge or dislike for you for no other reason that it feels you aren't pulling your fair share. Watch a well seasoned horse work as one half of the team with a learning youngster. If you pay attention you can see the older horse's impatience with the younger animal grow. You can see that, if the young horse lunges forward or refuses to pull its share, the older horse's ears will flatten and glaring looks will be shot towards the other. Evidence of the horse's responsiveness and understanding of the dynamics of its environment. If, in an extended long-term working relationship, you try hard to be consistent, and do your share, you will be surprised to see how willing, trusting and friendly your equine work mates will become. If you are mindful of their comfort, and acknowledge their sensory contributions (allowing that what they see or smell is worth taking a few minutes to figure out), they will be

86

waiting at the gate or door to go back out to work. Most horses and mules enjoy work (certainly more than most humans) be- cause it affords them something interesting to do (so long as discomfort and abuse aren't associated with the work). As evidence of this fact; I worked two teams (4 abreast) daily for two weeks preparing seed bed. Then I made one of the teams comfortable with a small pasture and grain and nothing to do while I took the other team, on a corn planter, two fences away to work. All that day the idle team would race to the fence and nicker or watch as the other team pulled the planter. Never once did the working team make any gestures toward the idle team. Next day I

Bud Dimick and his horses enjoy a parade. Bud is our Central Oregon wheelwright.

traded teams and drilled a small corner into oats and noticed that the horses had switched attitudes and that yesterday's idle team seemed perfectly content to pull the small drill and the now idle horses were anxious to be with us. These examples don't go near far enough to illustrate what I mean when I say that regular "constant" work makes for an important difference and changes both horses and teamsters. If for no other reason, it does at least allow that they honestly get to know one another.

Another important aspect of "extended" work is that it functions as a great equalizer. I suggested earlier that I felt training was never over. I might word that more directly;

YOU TRAIN A HORSE OR MULE WITH EVERY MOMENT THAT YOU SHARE.

No matter how old an animal is, or how good or bad its initial introduction to working procedures may be, your every action and shared moment with the horse is another thin layer applied to the animal's experience. And the animal's total experience is the reservoir it must go to for its language of response to circumstance and command. The two most important experiences (or layers) for the individual animal are:

      1. its most horrific;

      2. its most recent.

Often you can't know the nature of the "horrific" because you can't get that far into the animal's mind. But you can darn sure know "its most recent" and be responsible for the next. But we are too often

Charley Jensen and his Percheron team get ready to experiment with an unusual combination riding-walking plow. Good horses make such "inquiries" a real pleasure.

Lynn and Jess adjust the hitch on a disc plow as the horses wait patiently.

cumbersome in, and with, our best intentions. I believe that if we can be observant and caring and take the animal out and put it to honest work, for days on end, we provide the best environment for giving the animal a strong "most recent" experience to draw upon. Anything else we might do is contrived at best and misdirected at worst.

Well, I've gotten a little removed from my intention of defining "broke horses" but I still have some difficulty in sharing these heart-felt, and learned, beliefs I hold about good work horses. I can only hope that talking about what "makes" good horses does share with you, however, indirectly, what a "good" horse is.

In almost every case, whenever we hear some experienced horseperson speaking about a truly special animal with which they have worked, they speak of the animal's spirit and intelligence, not of its subservience or training. They speak of its capacity, or hunger, for interesting work, not of its 'dumb' nature. They talk about the amazing ways that this animal displays its abstract understanding of the limitations and possibilities of the "job", not of how much smarter we are. And I have a theory, born of my experience, that says that the number of recognized exceptional horses is directly proportionate to the number of exceptional humans doing the recognizing. In other words; if we had more exceptional teamsters, we'd have more exceptional horses.

It is important to make this rather negative point: A majority of self-proclaimed "horsepeople" are insensitive, scared, heavy-handed louts that ought to be pumping gas, or repairing computers and video machines, rather than subjecting horses to their empty-headed ways. Most "difficult" horses are made that way.

On the flip side: It is just possible that some average animals have had the opportunity to excel as team-mates to very sensitive, intelligent teamsters.

Twenty years ago I used to think that all those fragile, soft-spoken, old men with arthritic hands, who worked big horses with such apparent ease, were the lucky owners of some darned well broke horses. And, in turn, I also thought that cruel, ironic, coincidence was the only explanation for all those well-broke horses that came apart at the seams when transferred to the apparently qualified hands of young, strong, arrogant teamsters. The subtlety of quiet, assured, self-confidence reinforces any relationship born of, or susceptible to, trust.

And that is what a "good broke horse" is; one hard-working, willing component of a trusting relationship. As such, the possibilities are boundless.

What to Expect of a Well-Trained Work Horse

A.) It will go forward when asked.

B.) It will stop when asked.

C.) It will stand quietly when you want it to (hitching, harnessing, etc.).

D.) It will back when asked.

E.) It will not run away.

F.) It will want to work.

G.) It will start the load smoothly and quietly.

H.) It will take an interest in the work.

How Long Will It Take to Train a Work Horse?

A horse can be made to work in one day. A horse can be given a sound basic training in one week. It takes two to three months of successful driving at various tasks before a horse can be considered well trained. To properly "finish" a horse can take 6 months to 18 months. And all horses are in permanent training for their whole working life.

What are the Risks with Training Work Horses?

A.) If you do it wrong you may cause great harm to that horse's working future.

B.) If you don't employ common sense and exercise caution you could be seriously injured.

C.) If you ignore the important details you will fail.

Can You Do It?

I can't answer that. Only you can. I can tell you that common sense will aid you more than cleverness - and a sensitive nature more than physical strength - and self confidence more than arrogance.

Jiggs Kinney's good Iowa Belgian mares wait patiently by the forecart as their owner tells stories with the author.

Missouri's Richard Morrison drives four mules abreast on a forecart and brillion roller seeder.

Chapter Six

Differing Systems of Training

How many different approaches can there be to training horses? The list is infinite, or nearly so, because every individual human's personalized approach to each horse may be

unique. And this is as it should be. You must be prepared to customize your approach to the needs of the animal you're working with. There might be radical differences in approach or technique as stemming from assessments of the animal's limitations or capabilities or personality. And you will learn strong examples of this in the following chapters.

How many different training systems are there? I am sure I cannot answer that question and I have been studying the subject for 15 years. But I have noticed categories of systems that, although certainly not all-inclusive, have helped me to organize this presentation.

Submission

Submission

Many famous and effective horse trainers through the ages have based their systems on the assumption that the primary goal was to force the dumb horse to submit to man's rule and control. Over a span of 200 years millions of good horses resulted from these systems. Many failures also resulted.

Mutual Acceptance

A few dozen famous horse trainers (and hundreds not so famous) have based their systems on the complex assumptions that the primary goal was to

Acceptance

result in mutual acceptance with the trainer "accepting" the horse as partner and the horse "accepting" the trainer as dominant partner. With this system it is a given that the horse has intelligence.

Get-It-Done

Get-It-Done

Uncountable thousands of farmer, stockmen/trainers have based their systems on the simple reality that they had to "get-it-done" and weren't to be bothered with fancy philosophics or notions. How good any horse resulted was in direct proportion to the compassion and common sense of that farmer / stockman / trainer. Some of the very best trainers have come from this camp - and so have some of the worst. And most of the work horses, good, great and bad, of these last two centuries have come from this training and experience pool.

With the brief descriptions offered it would be reasonable to observe that there doesn't seem to be much difference between submission and acceptance. And perhaps even between those two and the "get-it-done" system. But I must respectfully submit that there is a great deal of difference and the two keys to seeing it rest with these notions:

1.) the advantage of a closely held guiding philosophy.

2.) the idea that we need to learn to "accept" the individual horse as partner.

(There are, of course, other important indicators but they are secondary to these two.)

A closely held guiding philosophy provides the trainer with a sort of filtration system which helps to keep the training goal(s) in sight and rule out naturally occuring or suggested deviations. For example: If the goal is to end up with a horse who likes and accepts you, impatience and punishment could push that goal further away.

As for the idea that we need to learn to "accept" the horse as partner; this is a radical notion that, if kept perpetually in view, affects how we see and treat the horse at every juncture in its' training. Success with such a notion demands that we work, no matter how accurate, to "undersand" the horse's behavior and needs.

Although I obviously believe in the mutual acceptance system that in no way should be taken to mean that I am denigrating the other two. From my experience and observation I must say that the exceptional people of each system are closer to one another than the language suggests. The "submission" trainer who is most effective will often be seen as someone who cares a great deal for the animal and values the animal's trust. The "mutual acceptance" trainers with the best records of success are those who are always insisting on compliance from their horses. And the "get-it-done" folk with the most successful trainees to their credit employ both submission and acceptance without thinking about it.

A good trainer is a good trainer. A good horseman is a good horseman. There is no only way to do anything. Effectiveness as a trainer and horseman comes best from a broad education married to sensitivity and it has nothing to do with camps, system labels or formulas. In fact, I would have to go so far as to say that the best horsemen or women have such wonderful, finely-tuned, natural understanding of horses that "systems" and "philosophies" for training can get in the way. Following their instincts leads them to and through effective contradictions over and over again. I have seen nearly every imaginable rule broken with good horses resulting. I know exceptional trainers who honestly cannot communicate what they do and when, because their knowledge is intuitive and instinctual - it follows no plan or system.

But we are dealing, in this book, with an effort to quantify, qualify and communicate to a large number of people the broadest mix of information on training and that includes outlines of systems and philosophies. Each individual set of experiences will, of course, determine whether or not ANY system guides you through the remainder of your career with horses.

Lynn and daughter Juliette with Thomas "Thom" Jefferson on the lead shank a few years back.

Kids and Horses

We are human beings, all of us, and as such prone to the lofty as well as the petty, to the high and mighty as well as the silly and petulant. We have our quirks and individual rigidities. One of mine comes with a philosophy that sees training horses and parenting children to be more similar than not.

I consider myself to be a moderately successful parent. But there is nothing moderate about my feelings for fatherhood, I love the responsibility and the place of it. I consider myself to be a moderately successful farmer/stockman trainer of work horses. And my feelings for that work are akin to that of parentage.

For some fifteen years I have heard a similar compliment-as-exemption from many different folk. The words vary but the meaning is the same:

"You are so lucky to have such well-behaved children. They are so sociable and polite. You could never get mine to be like that."

and

"You are so lucky to have such gentle well-behaved horses. And they like you. You could never get mine to be like that."

I said "compliment-as-exemption" because with a nod and a smile folks are saying that they too could be successful as parent and/or horse trainer if they started with well-behaved children and/or horses. They miss the point that this is the result of good parenting and training - not the place to begin.

And this is the part that is so hard to swallow.

What makes good kids and good horses is:

denial, opportunity, work, self-assurance, comfort, love, good expectations

or

barriers, open doors, work, self-confidence, comfort, caring, good expectations

or

restrictions, allowances, work, identity, comfort, admiration, good expectations

or

rules, throughways, work, personality, comfort, friendship, good expectations

Pick your list. They all add up to the same. And notice they all start the same because what I'm saying with "denial," "barriers," "restrictions" and "rules" is that the first lessons come from placement of obstacles, from saying "No."

"No you can't go that way or that way."

And next comes "Yes." "Yes you can go that way" - or opening up opportunities.

For horses and children understanding limitations from the very beginning builds a platform for:

1.) an acceptance of work.

2.) a development of their self-confidence.

3.) an appreciation of comfort given or allowed or created.

4.) the ability to give admiration and friendship in return.

5.) a working sense that the job can get done and get done well.

The difference of course is that most children are catapulted by or from their parental guidance into worlds apart and independent. Work horses we guide and train may remain as partners (or remain with other handlers).

There are elements of differing innate (or born) personalities in horses that can affect their individual receptiveness to training (and exceptions always exist) but as a rule the gentle, well-behaved, self-assured, friendly horse is **made** through training.

The Work Horse Is Made Through Training

I have spoken repeatedly of my penchant to work, in training horses, for "mutual acceptance." It is possible, up to this point, that some readers have concluded that my approach is one of "tolerance" and "gentleness" and "all forgiving." We can, each of us, get lost in the meaning of these words. Rather than react to them I would offer these precepts:

I expect the horse to do as I wish, when I wish.

I give appreciation, admiration and friendship freely.

I tolerate no behavior which carries risk of harm to me or the horses.

I look for, and applaud, the smallest evidence of success.

Though I work to avoid abuse, I will use the means necessary to enforce the rules of our work together.

I see these precepts as pieces of a successful etiquette of working horses.

Foundation Training versus   Work as the Trainer

There are those who believe that the repetition of hard work is all that is required to train a horse for harness. Although I do believe in regular work for the finishing of a trained horse, I do not personally believe in it as a solitary training tool. Not if we mean, by "training", that we're teaching the horse what's expected of him and getting good willing behavior in return. There is a list of common complaints from people having difficulty working horses, they come in the form of these questions:

1. *How do I get my horse to stand still?*
2. *How do I get my horse to move over in a stall?*
3. *How do I stop my horse from kicking?*
4. *How do I get my horse to come to me and allow me to halter it in a pasture?*
5. *How do I get my horse to be less afraid of dragging something behind?*
6. *How do I get my horse to let me pick up his feet?*

The answers to all of these questions are elementary to foundation training. In other words, horses behaving in the manner suggested by the questions are probably NOT ready for work in harness because they have little or no FOUNDATION training.

"But," I hear in retort, "I've been working this horse for quite a while! This horse is broke."

Just because you have been able to get a harness on the animal, hook him to something and make him pull it doesn't mean he's well-trained (though he may be "broke" by some loose definition of the word.) He's well trained when the above behavior questions disappear (or never appeared in the first place).

And the only way "hard work" alone will solve these problems or avoid them is if it is performed for years by a knowledgeable and lucky person. Whereas, a well-conceived, concentrated program of training WILL result in the horse having a "foundation" of manners and knowledge in days or weeks.

With hard work you get a tired uncaring animal who isn't paying attention, he or she is just trying to get through the day - so when you push or yank they follow.

With training the object is to have the full attention of a fresh alert animal when you take a "lesson plan" its way. In this way the lessons are learned and remembered. Here's what you can expect from a complete foundation training:

1. *Move ahead on voice command (without halter, headstall, ropes or lines.)*
2. *Stop on voice command and with no physical restraints.*
3. *Stand quietly without physical restraints.*
4. *Stand quietly, without restraint, and accept:*
    a.) *haltering*
    b.) *harnessing*
    c.) *harness adjustment*
    d.) *grooming*
    (all again, without restraint)
5. *Allow us to pick up each foot.*
6. *Want to be with us and will often follow without lead.*
7. *Accept a bit.*
8. *Move ahead on voice command.*
9. *Turn with line pressured on bit.*
10. *Accept pulling something on the ground from behind.*
11. *Deal with threatening panic.*

Because of this "foundation" training the actual job of first hitching to an implement or vehicle is less stressful and confusing to the animal. This often results in a very smooth and quiet transition to the "real world" of work.

But this is just one way to approach training. And there are a multitude of effective variations possible. In chapter fourteen (**Training System Variations**) I have gathered together information, presentations and comments on several unique and remarkable training systems which employ different philosophies.

Chapter Seven

Notes on Starting Foals, Young Horses, and Older Horses

In the following four chapters we will be dealing with four different age categories and several objectives. The age categories are important because they represent definite mental (or cognitive) parameters for the animals.

Often it is more difficult to teach a young foal (4 to 18 mos. - weanling/yearling) than the **new born** foal or older youngster (18 to 36 mos. - 2 year old). It takes more time, skill and patience to teach the weanling/yearling. Lessons must be repeated more often to be fully ingrained and retained because the young animals don't want to pay attention. However, contrary to prevalent previously held opinions, I believe through experience and observation that the properly trained weanling/yearling proves to grow into a superior workhorse. And that the properly imprinted newborn foal, handled and trained throughout its first two years can result in the ULTIMATE workmate. It is certainly true that the horse three to five years old which has received <u>no</u> training is almost always the EASIEST animal to train (we'll cover this in upcoming chapters). But the fullest relationship with the human workmate seems a bit illusive when starting with the untouched mature horse.

Regardless of age of the animal one interesting constant points to important conclusions.

The late Everett Hildebrandt of Waverly, Iowa with his last Belgian mare and foal. He was one of the great self-made, get-it-done, horsemen and trainers of the twentieth century.

97

The constant:

There appears to be a direct correlation between levels of initial resistance to training and the strength of the lesson learned. The harder the individual horse is to train the more likely the horse will be superior when training is finally accepted.

The conclusion:

Resistance to training may be an exercise in independence or a propensity to fear. As an exercise is independence you have a demonstration of superior intelligence. As a display of fear you have an opportunity to provide a strong bond when aiding the animal to handle that fear.

The training program outlined in the next four chapters covers our "mutual acceptance" approach as might be specific to the age of the individual animal. Chapter twelve, entitled "Follow Through to Finish", covers hitching, extended driving, and work as the routines for these may apply to animals of all age groups.

One of Jiggs Kinney's Belgian foals escapes his Columbus Junction, Iowa, barn.

Chapter Eight

Imprinting and Training
New Born Foals

We are actually talking about foals up to 4 mos. of age but there is a critical subdivision which covers the foal's first day after birth. We talk of the entire first 4 mos. as a training period.

GOAL

You need to identify your specific goals in training this youngster. For example: Will the foal be expected to handle a public setting (parades, horse shows, etc.)? Do you want to halter break the foal and then turn it loose until it grows up? Are you going to need to work the mother either away from, or with, the foal? Answers to these questions will determine how much repetition will be used and what level of training will be sought.

TIME REQUIRED

The least amount of time necessary would be three 15 minute sessions on the first day of life for imprinting.

An ideal situation would invoke regular daily handling, in and out of stabling, for a few minutes each day for anywhere from 2 weeks to 2 months.

SETTING

For newborn imprinting no special setting is required as long as safety and a strong respect of maternal instincts guide you. For later halter training the photos and diagrams are self-explanatory.

EQUIPMENT

A small comfortable suitable halter. A 10 foot long lead rope with a large snap, a grooming brush, 12 to 14 foot of soft cotton rope (3/8" to 5/8").

IMPRINTING

Much has been written, these last 10 years, about imprinting new born foals. I have not found any concrete evidence of the origins of this notion but it would seem to go back at least 25 years (and perhaps centuries by other names).

IMPRINTING refers to a simple process that takes advantage of the acute receptibility of new born foals to external stimulus. During the first hours after birth the gentle comprehensive handling of the foal, including breathing into its nostrils, imprints you, in particular and humans in general, as an acceptable (even necessary) part of the young equine's world. Imprinting most definitely works to advantage, and of course varies depending on the individual animal. Imprinting usually results, at the very least, in the foal being unafraid or less afraid of humans.

I believe in, and have practiced on our horses, an extended **IMPRINTING** process with excellent results. That "extended" process is described as follows:

If you are available at the birthing and have offered any reassurances to the mare, the imprinting

Correct way to hold a new born foal

process will be easy. First, when the foal is still wet touch it gently along the flat of the neck, breath gently into its nostrils and speak softly with long passages and lots of words. It doesn't matter what you say as long as you work at being soothing, just as you might with a new born child. The mare may watch you and be somewhat anxious but that should subside. Her natural instinct is to protect her baby from harm. When the foal accepts you, and the mare knows you, the perceived harm disappears. Also by handling the foal immediately after birth, you lessen the chance of interference from the concerned mare as she should be physically exhausted at this time.

Following the first contact, leave the mare and foal alone for whatever time it takes for the foal to stand and dry. At this time return to the foal

Respect the new mother's territorial imperative. Do not force yourself between the foal and its' mother. Be clever and reassuring to the foal and the mare.

and repeat the previous routine. You may, depending on the mare's manner, need to have her haltered and held (don't tie her) by someone. Always allow that the mare be near the foal as separating them at this time convinces the mare that you are a threat and can compound difficulties the next time you approach the foal. With the mare held by someone else, put one hand on the foal's chest and the other hand around the butt (as in drawing). With this "hold the foal" posture restrain the foal while you talk to it. Keeping your hand on the chest to restrain forward motion raise your other hand and lightly scratch above the tail until the foal raises its nose to say YES. Then move your hand over the back and scratch at the withers. The foal will enjoy this. Now lean forward and allow the foal to smell you. By doing this after the enjoyed scratching you intro-duce yourself to the youngster as the one who is bringing comfort. Now slip on a halter, it's easy with the newborn, and leave it for a couple of minutes while you return to those scratching areas but this time with a brush. In this way the foal associates the halter with pleasure. Now take the halter off and put it back on two or three times. With your hand on its chest run your other hand over all parts of the foal including the ears, tail and down the legs. Now brush it a little in order that the last thing you do in this lesson be pleasurable.

Remove the halters and leave mare and foal alone for 3 or 4 hours. This entire exercise with the foal shouldn't take over 15 minutes.

Now for the third and final imprinting session of the foal's first day of life. Repeat everything done in the previous session and include the added steps of picking up each foot in a calm, matter of fact and comfortable way. If the foal struggles make sure you are not causing harm but don't release the foot until there is a sign of acceptance. The slightest hesitation or stiffness on the part of the foal is enough of a sign, release the foot. In this way you are establishing that the path of least resistance is the best path.

Accomplishments: With this formula for extended imprinting you have:

1. imprinted yourself as familiar friend to foal and mare
2. accustomed foal to handling
3. introduced the grooming process to foal
4. introduced the halter, and haltering, as friendly
5. introduced harmless restraint
6. introduced the process of allowing feet to be picked up - all in the foal's first day of life.

If circumstances do not permit you to imprint on first day of foals' life, remember that anyone else knowledgeable may do the same routine for you with similar benefits. The object is to take full advantage of that fragile

101

mysterious window that opens for the foal with birth. It seems that for a few precious hours the foal is searching for, and sensitive to, any information about the components of its new life. And after this window closes, the foal relys on its mother (and friends - that's you) to offset and augment compelling instincts for survival.

Earliest training

If the imprinting opportunity is lost and you are dealing with a foal that is days or weeks old you need to take the same lessons to him or her but it will be a little more difficult, require greater caution, and more careful repetition.

Catching the foal in a nonpunitive way the first time requires a little common sense. Take the mare, with foal following, into a barn space or corral pen.

As in diagram walk the foal and mare into a corner space free of anything which might harm them. A box stall or double tie stall or corner will work. Halter and tie up mare. Keep foal in the corner with mare and calmly, but matter of factly, scratch and stroke the mare until foal

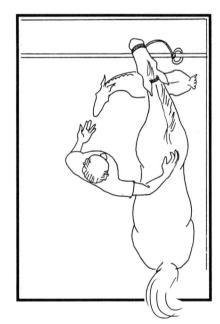

is near enough for you to scratch it at withers or above the tail. Be patient, be persistent, be careful and be kind. Always be mindful of mare's attitude and your position.

Check your foal halter, to see if you can buckle and unbuckle it quickly. Next (see photos) unbuckle halter and hold it under the foal's neck. Be careful not to touch the foal with the halter. With opposite free hand scratch the withers until the foal seems subdued then quietly reach over the neck with that same hand, careful to avoid touching the foal, and take hold of the poll strap of the halter. Now in a quick smooth move lift the basket of the halter forward and up over the foal's nose. The foal will probably move ahead quickly and a little startled - you must stay with it and buckle the halter quickly. Then release the foal. DO NOT attempt to hold it at this point. Let the foal get used to this new thing on its head.

At least 15 minutes later with lead rope return to the foal (still haltered) and, mindful of the mare, kneel down and talk to the baby horse - it will eventually come to you out of curiosity. Hold out the flat of one hand and with the other hold the opened lead rope snap. When the foal sniffs the flat hand quickly snap the rope to the halter ring. When the foal jumps back do NOT pull on the lead rope, instead follow the foal with slack in the rope. When the foal goes near its mother scratch the youngster and casually move into the "hold the foal" posture. Lay the still fastened lead rope across the foal's back and go through the same procedural routine used in IMPRINTING (see beginning of this chapter.)

By avoiding the use of the lead rope to hold or restrain the foal you will refrain from setting up a tug of war contest that might alienate the highly impressionable foal.

In these photos I am demonstrating with a four month old stud colt, Ben, who has been fully imprinted at birth. There are two values to these photos. One is to show how you might halter a new born foal (granted Ben is a little large). And the other is to demonstrate the incredible strength of the imprint training. Ben has not been handled for three months. Keep in mind that I have approached Ben in a 80 acre pasture and his mother has wandered off. There is no invisible wire or super glue holding him to this spot. He is held here by the strength of his training.

You should be doing this in a box stall or small enclosed area if the foal is untrained.

Haltering Foals

A. Approach and stroke and scratch the neck and withers.

C. When you pull the basket over the nose an untrained foal will back up quickly. You need to be prepared and committed to stay with, it backing up until you have fastened the halter. Then let go. Don't worry about restraining the youngster right away.

B. Hold the basket of the halter under the nose and the poll strap in your right hand (careful not to make sudden contact with the neck or ears). You want to be sure you can attach or buckle the halter smoothly and quickly. Check this before you try to halter.

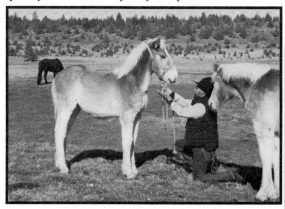

D. Then kneel down with both hands extended, in one hand have a open snap at the end of a lead rope. When the foal sniffs your hand snap the rope to the halter and release, do not pull on the rope.

E. When the foal lets you return to scratch its back gently reach for the rope and hold it slack.

103

F. After the foal is comfortable with me hanging around I work to get it accustomed to lots of foolery. Here I have put the rope in Ben's mouth, like a bit, and let him mouth it.

G. I stroke him all over, including the chest and belly. He likes this.

H. I stroke his forehead and...

I. ...move up to his ears. This will pay dividends later in life for bridling or any work around the head.

J. And finally I pick up his feet. Notice he's still out in that pasture. To the left of him is Juniper, his full sister, and behind him is Belle his half sister.

Ben is a stallion prospect so I am particularly pleased with his training progress. If you haven't noticed these things please do take note: He was appraoched and haltered in the center of a big field. He is a nursing foal and his mother is no where in sight. He offered only full acceptance of what ever I took to him. When I was done, and unhaltered him, he did not run away. Instead he started to follow me until he lost interest and walked off with his half sister. If I had the time, and chose to, I could harness him and drive him and he would accept it and benefit from the extra training. I will not attempt to work him until he is three years old. But I expect that when that time comes he will offer no resistance.

The way to measure how well the foal is doing is to look for signs of acceptance. Is the foal enjoying your contact? Does the foal look to you, or begin to follow, when you leave? When you do get some sign of acceptance employ the butt rope to teach the foal to lead. Do this in a restricted area like a barn alley. The principle behind this tool is simple. Instead of pulling on the lead you give a voice command to go and apply a soft pressure on the hips under the tail. The foal will move away from the pressure on its hind end and into the open door you provide. This is why its important not to jerk on the lead rope and confuse the foal. Use the lead rope as a restraint of last resort and to offer indications of change in direction. If the foal rushes ahead and you yank on the lead rope to stop it you have succeeded in confusing the little guy. First you make him go then you make him stop--what do you want? Instead when you start the foal be prepared to release the butt rope pressure, maintain a slack lead and stay with the foal offering reassuring words. Believe me its a big enough step to get the youngster to go with you on the lead, there's no need to confuse it with other restrictions and actions. If you're working in a suitable restricted space all should proceed okay. Remember to offer regular praise and reassurance along with scratching.

Side Bar
NO TUG OF WAR

One of the keys to successful training of any horse is a constant effort to avoid any one-on-one contest of strength and will and instead to employ "obstacles" and "open doors". "Obstacles" include anything we might use or do that makes it difficult for the horse to proceed in a certain direction or way. If we stand in front of the horse and block its path we are making ourself into an "obstacle". "Open doors" include clearly offered opportunities. If we let the horse pass in a certain direction at a certain time we are providing an "open door."

Pulling on a lead rope fastened to the obstinate haltered foal provides no obstacle and no open door only confusion and contest. If we can find a way to make following us a logical path, an open door, we are building a positive relationship while training. One example is the use of a "butt rope". (See photos on page 167.)

You will need to gauge how well the individual foal is responding to your handling to determine when to use the butt rope for training to lead. (See Sidebar entitled Measuring Progress).

Side Bar
Measuring Progress During Training

Whether you train only one horse or several dozen an important tool will be your general perceptiveness. You need to be able to honestly evaluate how well the individual trainee is progressing in general and has progressed in the last lesson. And this is a case that calls for dramatically lowered expectations because it is critical that you recognize the smallest change as significant. The reason this is important is because taking the next steps in training to an unprepared animal can cause a setback. What you are looking for is clear evidence that a given lesson is being learned. If it isn't, the lesson must be repeated. And remember the younger the animal - or the smarter the animal - the more likely the lessons will have to be repeated.

Side Bar
Teaching the Haltered Foal/Horse to Back

As demonstrated in these photos, to teach the haltered foal to back simply place yourself in front of it and with the flat of your hand extended, like a blade, push on the point of the shoulder as you say "back" and apply a quick little backward tug on the lead rope. The foal will actually be responding to the pressure on the shoulder and your presense in front as it chooses the path of least resistance and backs. With deliberate repetition of the verbal command "Back", and the backwards tug on the halter it shouldn't take too long before the foal will not need the touch on the point of the shoulder. And soon all that will be required is the verbal command. This is a very important lesson, one which helps to reinforce the overall "foundation" training, as well as figuring in later when the youngster grows into a work harness.

Teaching the Foal to Lead: The Butt Rope

We are using a weanling Percheron filly for this demonstration so that the white Butt Rope will show up well. But this device works on month old foals or ten year old horses.

A. A lead rope is snapped into the halter and stretched out to my left hand. The butt rope, a large diameter soft cotton from twelve to sixteen feet long, has both ends passed through the chin strap of the halter.

B. Here you can see the Butt rope hanging over the withers of Kate. In my left hand I hold both ends of the rope and can easily pull slack out of it.

C. Here you can see how I've crossed the rope at the withers and pulled the loop end back over the hips.

D. The Butt rope is completed and in position under the tail. I give the filly a verbal command to go and if she refuses I give a quick jerk on the two ends of the butt rope (NOT on the lead rope). She feel a push on her butt and responds by moving away from it, or forward. I keep repeating until she is willing to go ahead on voice command alone.

Also remember to use the same verbal command every time you set to go. And every time you stop, or feel the foal is going to stop on its own, say WHOA.

After the foal picks up on the forward motion business you can begin training for WHOA. Training to stop is easier than training to go. With this small foal you have tremendous leverage on the lead rope. But we don't want to use the rope unless it's absolutely necessary. Instead we'll go back to "obstacle" and "open door". When you want the foal to stop step in front of it, with loose lead, and say whoa. The second time you do this say WHOA first - then step in its path. Repeat this exercise until the foal offers to stop with voice command alone. When that happens don't step in front, instead stroke the foal's neck and say thank you.

The younger the foal the quicker it will learn. The older the foal the more often you'll have to repeat lessons.

You can use these lessons with any foal up to four months of age. Beyond four mos. and up to 18 mos. there are some important, even critical, differences. But before we get into those, we should measure what this procedure has done for us.

Accomplishments:

Same as imprinting plus

1. halter training complete
2. trained to pick up feet
3. trained to go on command
4. trained to stop on command
5. self confidence taught.

Chapter Nine

Training Weanlings/Yearlings

This age group goes from 4 mos. to 18 mos. And we must deal with two important distinctions.

1. Those who have not been handled before now or have been mistreated - "never been touched or touched badly."

2. Those who have been imprinted and/or trained as newborns.

Forgive me the analogy but imagine that you are dealing with human children from two years old to twelve years old which have never been given any training or discipline. Yes it can be that bad. Or imagine children of that age span who have been spoiled and allowed (even encouraged) to do whatever they want. Scary? Or imagine children who have been severely abused and are prone to panic, rage and/or terror. Luckily that's not so often.

It requires patience (loads of it), perseverance, understanding, forcefulness, kindness and more patience.

Goals:

May we presume that you will want to at least accomplish these?

1. Complete halter training, including easy to catch.

2. Full acceptance of you.

3. Able to pick up feet.

4. No kicking or biting.

And then we have some variables, depending on your decisions and needs which might include:

5. Courage to handle public settings (i.e. horseshows, parades).

6. Full acceptance of tie stall routine.

7. Acceptance of bit.

8. Acceptance of harness.

9. Preliminary driving training.

10. Able to pull something light.

As you can see there are many variables. Instead of dealing with all the possible combinations, we'll go through a complete routine and allow you to pick and choose what you wish. Please remember that the primary lessons (i.e. whoa, giddup, stand, total acceptance, etc.) are critically important. If you go for a shortcut, and try to do something advanced straightaway, you are asking for trouble.

TIME REQUIRED

Goals 1-4 could take an absolute minimum of three 1/2 hour sessions or go to ten 1/2 hour sessions depending on you and your animal.

Goals 5-10 will take from five 1/2 hour sessions to ten 1/2 hour sessions.

There are always exceptions which take longer or less time. And certain aspects, i.e. tie stall acceptance, are best accomplished as part of an extended care schedule although they can be trained for. Some training lessons can be accomplished while another animal is being worked with or simultaneously with 2 or 3 other horses.

SETTING

The ideal setting includes a round pen enclosure 30 to 45 feet across (45 is best) preferably 5 to 6 feet tall.

If you are dealing with animals which have never been handled you may need to configure a gate alley passage to the pen to allow you to herd them in. I believe strong, tall, open fencing or panels which allow the horse to see out are better than the solid enclosure because it does allow the horse some sense of choice and less chance that a claustrophobic panic will develop.

An experienced trainer can work within a rectangular space but the problems posed by the corners of the pen can be too much for the less experienced handler. The key is to know how to read the animal and back off when panic is near. A panicky horse heading into the "trap" that a corner represents is a situation that eliminates the objectives of a mutual trust approach. At all times the horse must have, or believe it has, a choice.

The setting should include some accommodation for tieing horses up at a feed manger outside of the round pen, preferably in a barn or shed. (See stable diagram in chapter three).

EQUIPMENT

Equipment needed depends on how far you wish to go. Suitable halter(s) and lead rope(s), 14' soft 3/8" to 5/8" cotton rope, 40 to 60 foot lariat (or similar rope), snaffle bit(s) with double snaps, suitable collar and harness with single lines, single tree with hook and chain.

Nursing foals

Your first objective will be to get the young horse to accept you. This will require that you may reasonably ask for the foal's total attention. For this reason I must encourage you not to undertake this training with a foal 4 mos. or older, which is still nursing. If you have to compete with a "where is my mama" panic and the mare's pleadings from the next pen, you will NOT be able to command attention and the training will be nearly impossible. It is best that, if the foal has not been handled at all to this point, you wait until weaning is complete. Four months old is not too early to wean.

Acceptance Training

Yes, you can train for (or to) acceptance - and yes ideally acceptance and compliance come throughout the entire training. But initially you need to demonstrate to the animal that you control its movement without punishment or physical harm. You do this by using an "obstacle" (or denial) and "open door".

> *At all times the horse must have, or believe it has, a choice.*

Herd the foal into the round pen, enter and close the gate. The two of you should be alone in this setting. If you have people watching ask them to step back from the fence and to be silent. If you have loud goings-on, immediately outside the pen, it will become a distraction that can confuse the foal.

Look at your watch. You do not want this lesson to be less than 15 minutes or more than 30. Closer to 15 is better. Too long a lesson can erase learning from the beginning of the session.

With the first lessons limit your verbal commands to WHOA and whatever sound you prefer to start your horses with. IMPORTANT: Be sure to use the exact same "go" or "giddup" and "whoa" commands - do not vary.

Approach the foal, raise your arm and give the command to go. As the foal moves to the fence and starts around you move to the center of the pen.

This is important. If and when the foal should hesitate and stop -immediately say WHOA. Whenever the foal starts to move give the command to go. You want to immediately begin taking credit for every decision the foal makes. A bit of sneakiness but it is important.

To start the foal move from the center and towards it with arm outstretched and the go command. As it moves you move back to the center of the pen. To stop the foal step ahead as if you would cross its path and say WHOA.

This is well illustrated in the photo series which follow. The first is entitled "Black Bob's First Time."

111

Acceptance Training: Black Bob's First Time

Black Bob is a 7 month old 3/4 Belgian - 1/4 Percheron stud colt. He has not had any handling. He was not imprinted at birth. This session in the round pen was his first lesson of any kind. He was weaned a month prior to this session.

A. From the center of the pen, I "kiss" to him and raise my hand. His natural reaction is to move away from me. It is important that he get a clear sense that I am "pushing" him away.

B. Bob shows no panic, he's simply moving away from me on my insistance. He does not feel trapped.

D. At this point he's figured out that I will be crossing his path and he starts to put on the brakes. I say WHOA in a strong voice.

C. I have started to cross the pen to head Bob off...

E & F. Bob stops and faces me.

112

G. Bob turns away from me to leave and I head that way with outstretched hand...

H. ...When I am in a position to block his travel I say WHOA and Bob's head comes up.

I. I stand still, but my position gives a message that forward is blocked. Bob sets to turn and I offer no resistance. I let him have an "opportunity".

J. As he turns I follow, calmly maintaining my distance. I am working to avoid the nonsense of panic. I want Bob to be able to think.

K. I follow knowing that, as long as Bob remains calm, he will stop when I am in a straight line with his eyes because he will feel I have checked his move...

L. When I get to that point straight across from his eyes I say WHOA and Bob stops. Tremendous success. I am controlling his movement and he's thinking.

113

M. Bob has turned his head slightly and is looking straight at me as I stand still. What you can't see is that I'm avoiding "hard" eye contact because it can make the horse nervous.

N. I haven't moved. Bob is turning slowly towards what he perceives is his opening or "opportunity" to leave.

O. When Bob makes his move so do I, calmly turning to head him off.

P. I go farther than I need to and when I say WHOA Bob stops and raises his head.

Q. I raise my hand and "kiss" at him to go. I "expect" him to MOVE when I say go and my voice and movement reflects this.

R. Bob thinks he can get away from me. I need to convince him I am in control. I am not trying to catch him or trap him, I am heading to a point where I can stop his forward motion. I will not say WHOA until I know it will coincide with him stopping.

S. At this exact point Bob has figured out that I am going to block his forward motion and he prepares to put on the brakes, a split second later I say WHOA.

T. As soon as he stops he starts to turn, still carrying "escape" energy but slowing down considerably.

U. I let him turn, because now is the time to allow him an "opportunity" or "choice". It is important to do this so that he does not get a sense of being trapped.

V. As he moves I follow, keeping my distance but picking up speed with the intention of reaching that spot, straight across from his eyes and "testing" his responsiveness to the verbal WHOA.

W. At this point you can see he's not speeding up. What I can read is that he's paying close attention to me and he's thinking, both excellent indicators.

X. I say WHOA and Bob stops. Always, I am working to control his movements naturally and without the extreme threat that might provoke a panic.

Y. *Quiet time, we both stand still as long as Bob is willing, but the instant Bob starts to move I give the command to go.*

Z. *As he turns I move to black his path...*

ZA. *Bob eyes me and seems to realize that I'm a smart, yet relatively harmless, mammal.*

ZB. *We've gone back and forth one more time and I know something is happening. here I'm talking in low monotanous tones and Bob thinks.*

ZC. *Great news as Bob seems to ask "Who are you anyway?" This is the time to stand still and do nothing. You are allowing an opportunity or opening for the foal to approach you.*

ZD. *Bob turns to face me. The beginning of a strong indication of conditional acceptance. The condition is that I respect him and not push the moment.*

ZE. (Top left) I reach forward with an offered hand and notice Bob leans back.

ZF. (Above) When I withdraw my hand he leans forward.

ZG. (Left) He takes a step forward and calmly disregards me by turning his head slightly.

ZH. (Below) The session is done. Bob has learned something about me. He has been introduced to WHOA and GIDDUP. He has demonstrated great intelligence. Most important, I am stopping when I should. I am very pleased with the progress.

Give the foal lots of opportunity to get to know you aren't a threat. Kristi is visiting with Belle and her mother Cali. That is three year old Polly behind her.

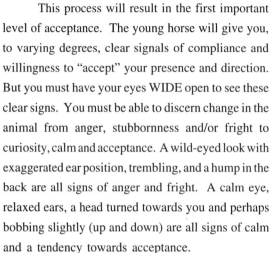

This process will result in the first important level of acceptance. The young horse will give you, to varying degrees, clear signals of compliance and willingness to "accept" your presence and direction. But you must have your eyes WIDE open to see these clear signs. You must be able to discern change in the animal from anger, stubbornness and/or fright to curiosity, calm and acceptance. A wild-eyed look with exaggerated ear position, trembling, and a hump in the back are all signs of anger and fright. A calm eye, relaxed ears, a head turned towards you and perhaps bobbing slightly (up and down) are all signs of calm and a tendency towards acceptance.

You are looking for signs of change to indicate to you that the next level of training is appropriate. If the horse is not ready you will not be able to do the next exercises.

Once you have acceptance go calmly and matter-of-factly to the youngster allowing it to smell you. Each individual animal is unique, some will permit your first touch to be on the nose or face. Others will not and instead prefer you stroke the neck first. But almost 95 percent will immediately welcome a scratch on the withers. You will have only your judgement and instincts to guide you.

After your first contact (remember it may come in one 15 minute session or in two or three 30 minutes sessions) return to the foal with halter and lead rope in hand BUT NOT WITH "CATCHING" IN MIND. Scratch and pet again and then turn and walk away. You are working at "winning" confidence instead of forcing yourself on the animal. You are carrying the rope and halter to accustom the horse to seeing you

Young, month old, Thomas "Thom" Jefferson on a loose lead and showing how well behaved and trained the fully imprinted and handled foal might be. His mother is standing quietly stabled in the barn behind him. Thom is featured as a four year old in the photo series in Chapter Eleven.

with it. After 2 or 3 of your approaches during which you stroke and scratch, the foal will look forward to your return and begin approaching you. You have made a friend.

If at this time the foal seems comfortable enough you may try to halter but THIS IS IMPORTANT - don't push it. The foal will give you ample indication of whether or not it's ready. The experienced horseperson can "push it" at this point without harm. But for the beginner it is important to understand how to gauge the foal's readiness for the halter and when to back off. If you allow the foal, through circumstance, to tell you no you've lost ground. So it's your job to "read" the foal.

Besides those obvious signs we spoke of before, signs which can be read from some distance, there are those you must "feel". When stroking the foal, again remember to be matter-of-fact so as to avoid "telegraphing" the wrong feeling to the foal. Try to think about something else, something neutral like apple pie or fishing. Run your hand ever higher up the neck. If you feel the foal tighten as though it might walk off, back your hand down only to return soon to that trigger spot. Keep doing this until the horse "accepts" you touching more and more. If you aren't able to gain more acceptance to touch with this process the animal is NOT ready for halter.

I've had foals where they'd allow me to play with their ears and lips, stroke their chin and eyelids, and wrap my arms around their neck before I attempted to put

on the halter. At that point it was very easy. I'm not saying you have to go that far but I hope it draws a picture for you of what I mean. You want this animal to like and accept you to that degree. And you want this animal to be less sensitive and apprehensive to what you bring to its head.

The next series of photos, "Black Bob's Second Time", is a good demonstration of just how slow the process might go and how much patience is required.

Following Bob is a series of photos, "Kit's lesson", which demonstrates how the process is used with an imprinted/halter trained foal for the purpose of establishing who is boss in a mutual acceptance relationship. These photos also demonstrate procedures for haltering.

The baby horse is a naturally curious creature to whom just about everything is new. Impressions are made quickly and they last. It is your challenge to make sure that you do not present yourself as a threat.

119

Acceptance Training: Black Bob's Second Time

*(Please refer to page 112 for background.)
Here I've returned to Bob for a second session. I have no specific goals in mind. I've left myself open to read him and determine how far to go. With the first session I figured out that Bob is an intelligent boy and I know from experience that this usually translates to it taking longer. But I also know that my patience will be richly rewarded in the depth and character of relationship I can expect with him later.*

A. Once in the pen Bob immediately faces me. An excellent sign, not necessarily one of compliance, but most definitely of intelligence and courage. I raise my hand and give the command to go.

B. As Bob turns to go I keep my distance from him but follow his direction knowing that when I get to that certain spot he will stop...

C. Again when I am straight in line with him, and he has perceived that my next move would put me in his path he stops and I make sure he hears me say WHOA as he stops.

D. (Above) As I raise my hand in preparation to ask him to go Bob raises his head in unison. He's giving me a strong indication of the degree to which he's paying attention. This is further indication of just how intelligent this little guy is.
E. (Right) As he turns to go I follow and say WHOA.

With this routine notice that I am anticipating his stopping and saying WHOA to coincide. In this way I am training him to associate the word WHOA with stopping. Same thing with the command to go.

F. (Above) Bob turns on the fence and I stand my ground offering no resistance, no obstacle. I'm giving him an open door. And what he does next is the surprise I've been waiting for...

G. Bob has turned completely around to face me, fully attentive, and unafraid. Curious, courageous and intelligent. He knows that I know. And I know that he knows. A big moment.

121

H. At this point I make the determination to squat down. Doing this often results in a boost in self-confidence to the trainee and allows them to exercise their curiosity...

I. ... And that's what happens with Bob as he reaches his neck forward to check me out.

J. He takes a step forward and then another...

K. And finally he's able to feel and smell my breath and touch my outstretched hand with his nose.

L. (Right) And now is when the patience comes into play again. Rather than push this important display of acceptance I choose to tell him goodbye and call an end to the session. I will return the next time and expect more, perhaps even haltering. But so far my accomplishments have been many.

A real trick with this approach to training is teaching yourself to be patient and know how to read success. Some who look at these photos may feel nothing has been accomplished. All I can do is point to this colt and many other horses and say that they are as reliable and as well-trained as they are today because I took this time and tact in the beginning.

Acceptance Training: Kit's Lesson

This weanling filly was a gift from my good friends Jess and Sharon Ross. They imprinted and halter trained Kit. Kit has been on a wagon train and in a parade and is accustomed to lots of people.

In this lesson I want to "push" Kit away from me and stop her on voice command and without restraint as an introduction to what she will experience when we start training her to drive. I have used her as a model to demonstrate a couple of other things for you.

One is how to approach the unknown filly and win confidence with pleasureable contact.

Another is a way to prevent the unknown foal from successfully escaping a haltering effort.

A. I have approached Kit and allowed her to sniff my open hand.

B. I have stroked her neck and scratched her withers finally ending up with a scratching above the tail always mindful of where I am and any body language she might give to indicate flight or attack. Flight is always the first choice of the equine, with rare exception attack is always in self-defense and is usually an acquired habit of the horse who's been allowed to get away with running people off.

123

C. I push Kit away but it's more difficult than with Bob because she's used to coming to me, so she cuts across the round pen. But I persist and am successful.

D. Using the same moves as with Bob I train her to associate WHOA with stopping.

F. So I approach her and make contact with her shoulder, preparing to reassure her...

E. Kit has gone through the back and forth routine enough times and I notice she's starting to get a little bothered. She doesn't understand why now she has to move away and stop on command. But it's critically important that she learn because these lessons will prevent her from becoming a pesty nuisance.

Even so I don't want to overdo it so I decide that she needs a little reassurance. Normally I want the foal to face me before I go to them but I decide to make exception in Kit's situation because she has had a great deal of handling.

G. ...and her reaction is to turn her butt to me for scratching. This is a bad habit so I push her away and give a sharp command to go. She moves away startled and we repeat the back and forth acceptance training routine.

H. Finally Kit turns to me and says 'I think I understand,' so I calmly approach her with a matter-of-fact posture. I don't want to sneak up on her or go to her begging her to accept me, I want to go to her like it's no big deal.

I. She waits for me with a tad bit of apprehension which is good and normal. It means she's paying attention to me.

J. I've turned her sideways so that you can see the next process easily. Notice I'm letting her sniff my hand.

K. I move forward and stroke her neck.

L. Now I position myself so that I can put the soft cotton lead rope across her withers. My left hand is on her chest so that she doesn't walk forward and away.

M. Here you can see the doubled halter rope laying across the withers. I am careful not to let it fall off and startle the filly.

125

N. Here I am pulling the lead rope around the filly's neck.

O. I've stretched it out so that you can see where it is. If this filly wanted to fly back this rope would not help me enough to hold her. So I'm counting on my relationship with her and her good behavior.

P. Now I'm moving my hand up the neck to pass the rope up higher where it will be more effective.

Q. When the rope gets up where it belongs she starts to pull back and I say WHOA and reassure her with a stroke on the neck..

R. With the rope over her neck I reach my right arm over to hold the poll strap of the halter while the basket is held in my left hand directly under her nose.

S. Here you see I've pulled the basket up and the poll strap over all in one motion. Fasten calmly and quickly.

The next series of photos once again illustrate the round pen acceptance training this time with Betsy, a weanling Belgian / Percheron filly. In this case Betsy was not imprinted but was halter trained as a nursing foal. In this situation I want her to learn to move away from me on command and stop with WHOA. She didn't want to move away so I've employed a slight variation in the program. Usually I separate the initial acceptance training from the next stage which involves a long rope. In Betsy's case I took the long rope in and used it to "push" her and then move direct into the "roping out".

I don't mean to confuse the routine with this variation but I do believe that you will have to customize your own approach to each individual animal. I hope this series will demonstrate that the system or procedure is not as important as the goal.

Acceptance Training: Betsy's Lesson

A. Betsy wants to be with me and she faces and then approaches. I do not want to confuse her so I approach, reassure her, and then go behind her with a command to go...

B. ...but she's slow to respond...

C. She wants to stop before I want her to, and she hesitates to go.

D. I need some help if I'm not to loose ground with her. So I pick up my lariat and flip it around some. It works - she's paying attention and moving away.

127

E. In this picture you can see that I no longer have any problem getting her to move and turn when I wish. I am NOT telling her WHOA at this point, I am simply blocking her path and pushing her away.

F. She comes to me fast and I raise my arms and give her a go command. This turns her away.

H. The rope bothers her and she doesn't let me finish my approach so I return to the routine of "pushing" her away, stopping her and allowing her opportunities to accept me and the rope.

G. We go back and forth a couple of times with my using the WHOA command successfully. Then I feel her loosen up and calm down and I stand still. The result is that she turns to face me and approach. I in turn approach with outstretched hand careful to keep my rope. I want her to accept it as well as me.

I. (Right) Here you can see how I drag the rope and move to that spot straight across from her eyes to stop her. When she puts on the brakes I say WHOA.

This whole exercise is helping me to gauge the intelligence of this filly. She has shown me a clear understanding that I alone am very different from I with a rope. Remembering that the difficult ones are often the best. I make a spur of the moment decision. If she does not allow me to approach her completely, with rope in hand, I will force the issue.

J. When she stops and faces me I approach calmly but with rope in hand and she leaves...

K. ..I move into position to stop her and for the first time she ignores my WHOA! This is bad and I can't afford to have her think she can do this.

L. I decide to throw the lariat, with the intention of looping her head and neck, but I DO NOT TIGHTEN the rope.

M. Instead, with the rope slack I continue to work her as before with the added dimension that I occasionally flip the rope around on her.

N. The result, in just a very few minutes is her total acceptance of the rope and me.

"Roping Out"

This should be done as a lesson in and of itself. Start out fresh and plan for 15 to 30 minutes.

Next comes the lariat. Again in the round pen put the loop of the lariat around the horse's neck and DO NOT TIGHTEN. In this procedure it is important that you never offer any restraint. You will NOT be snubbing down or tieing up this animal at this time.Make sure you are wearing gloves as you want the rope to slide freely through your hands..

Have the horse go away from you as you go to the center of the pen. You will be flipping the rope around and over the horse until it accepts whatever you dish out. Sounds extreme, I know, but the photos which follow should illustrate the effectiveness and the harmlessness. Because so much of this is repetitive and identical, from one age group to another, I've chosen to illustrate the "roping out" in outstanding photographic detail within the two chapters which follow. Please study these photo series before attemping this important procedure.

One of the advantageous features of the "*roping out*' procedure is that it provides excellent opportunites for training the foal to allow its feet to be handled. As soon as it has accepted the rope fully, put a loop around each pastern, and from a distance of at least twelve feet, pull on the rope until you lift the foot. You should be surprised to find that the fully accepting foal will stand still for this procedure. And you should expect some kicky-type resistance to the pull. Do not pull harder on the rope. Instead, with gloves on, hang on to the rope and ride the motion of the leg back and forth until the foal gives up, then and only then are you going to give the foot back. You do not want to hurt the foal. The drawings which follow, and then the photos in the next two chapters, will illustrate this process.

Initial Training to Handle Feet

As illustrated in this photo, after the rope exercises with the feet you should immediately begin picking them up by hand for short periods. Never let the foal take its foot away from you.

"Hosing Out"

A variation of "roping out" that may be done in warm weather with many of the same results is "Hosing Out".

*(I refer to these processes as **Roping Out** and **Hosing Out** because they are, in my estimation, evolved from "Sacking Out" and much preferred because of the important distinction that the trainee, in our program, is not completely restrained and a perception of choice is allowed and desired for best results.)*

I credit my good friend and outstanding Freisian trainer, Clay Maier, with introducing me to the calming advantages of directed water flow. This is the variation we've come up with: Take a garden hose into the round pen and have a second person on the lead shank of the haltered foal. DO NOT TIE UP THE FOAL. While scratching, stroking, and talking, run water on the foal's front feet until accepted. If, and when, the foal resists or moves away, stay with it. Do not allow the foal to stop the contact of the water. Then slowly run the water up a front leg. You want to end up able to run water (hard and soft) all over the animal's body with its full acceptance. Cool water on a hot day is easiest.

With Roping Out and Hosing Out we are teaching the foal how to deal with fear, to be less ticklish, to give its feet freely, and that we are in

132

friendly control. Critically important lessons in the game of acceptance.

Accomplishments to this point:

1. halter training begun/easy to catch
2. trained to pick up feet
3. trained to go on command
4. trained to stop on command
5. self confidence/courage training well started.
6. trained to stand quietly
7. trained not to kick or bite
8. full acceptance of you

Stabling

At the close of the first roping or hosing out take the foal to a tie stall or feed manger and tie securely. The foal must not be able to break free or a terrible habit may begin of flying or pulling back deliberately to try to get free. Make sure manger is well stocked with good hay. Because of previous recent lessons the young horse should stand quietly. To reinforce the pleasurable nature of stabling, brush the horse while it eats. If this is the first stabling experience do not leave the young animal unattended. Find something useful to do nearby if you've tired of brushing. When horse seems to tire of eating hay, and before any foolishness begins remove the horse to paddock, pasture, or pen. Avoid removing the horse BECAUSE it is carrying on a fuss. It is in this way that many people inadvertently train for bad habits.

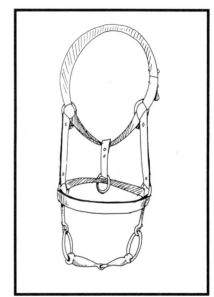

If it is possible to feed the youngster at the manger, and only at the manger, for the next few weeks you will have a terrific procedural aid and reinforcement for your training. If the foal is haltered and led to a stall in order to eat, and then must back out and be led back to freedom, you will speed the halter training and barn manners considerably.

Bitting

During the second or third stabling session fasten a snaffle bit into the halter with double snaps (see illustration) and leave it so that the foal must learn to eat with it in the mouth. This will greatly reduce difficulties with the bit during the

Sidebar
Bit and cold weather.
Never put a frozen steel bit in a horse's mouth. Make sure it is at least warm enough to be comfortable to the touch.

first driving exercises. Again do not leave the animal unattended while tied and with a bit in its mouth.

Harness and Driving the Youngster

If you've determined that you want to train the young horse of this age group to drive in harness please keep in mind that if they are made to pull heavy loads before 3 to 4 years of age it can be damaging to their bones, cartilage, and overall future physical development That said, I encourage you to train horses at an early age to drive and pull light vehicles or implements for short periods. Comprehensive early training makes for wonderfully well behaved and reliable 3, 4 and 5 year olds.

First Harnessing

Return to the round pen with the haltered young horse, the harness and the lariat. Remove the halter, stroke the horse and move it away from you. Hang the harness in some convenient spot on the inside of the round pen. Return the the foal. Check to see the horse's responsiveness to your commands to go and whoa. Repeat the initial "acceptance training" from earlier this chapter.

You should see, almost immediately, the degree to which the youngster has retained and remembered. If the foal is quick to turn to you in acceptance, go to it and reward with kind words and stroking. Now slip the loop of your lariat over its head and repeat the "roping out" procedure. As soon as you get a clear indication of the complete acceptance of the horse to the whirling, slapping rope go to him or her and remove the rope, stroke and halter. Tie a lead rope on the halter and let it hang on the ground. Now walk away towards the harness, if the horse tries to follow simply turn and say WHOA. You want that horse to stay just as you might a well-trained dog.

In this process it is _not_ important that the collar and harness fit perfectly but some effort should be made to avoid harness that is too small.

Approach the horse, in a matter of fact manner, with the unbuckled collar and allow it to be seen and smelt before slipping up and on the neck. The horse should, and will, stand still unless you hurt or surprise it. Now return to page 76 and follow this schedule for harnessing.

Now remove the lead rope and move foal away from you allowing it to move around the pen freely in its new clothes. This will allow the foal to become accustomed to carrying this new stuff (harness) on its back.

Next fasten bit into halter and fasten on single driving lines at least 20 feet long. Now step back and give the horse the customary command to go. You are not expecting the horse to perform properly, you are allowing it a safe environment in which to become accustomed to the harness and the act of moving away from you with a bit in its mouth and lines attached. So if the youngster should bolt do NOT try to stop it or turn it just follow with "perfect tension" on the lines.

This is the point where it becomes critical that you have some driving experience before attempting to teach the horse to drive. If you don't you should skip ahead to the second half of this text entitled TRAINING TEAMSTERS.

Allow the horse to continue and watch how it will gradually slow and prepare to stop. Time it so that the very second the horse stops on its own you say WHOA. This and other important aspects of early driving training will be much more apparent when you review the photos in the next two chapters. You first session will be a success if you can get your trainee to move away from you on command and stop on command.

For the finesse and suggested routines to advance the driving lessons please refer to the photos in Chapter Eleven.

> *Learn to accept progress in little doses or steps. Stop while you're ahead. Make sure the last few minutes of the lesson are wholly successful no matter how simple. Do not quit a lesson with the horse's refusal or misbehavior. Stop on a positive note, no matter how small.*

Second Harnessing Session

You may return to a horse with new lessons several times a day but you should allow at least two hours to pass between each lesson. And ideally the horse should not be stabled or tied up during this rest or off period. You do not want your student to become sullen or depressed as this may lead to a balky mood. You want an alert student, fresh and healthy, for each session.

Before the second harnessing, again in the round pen, you need to gauge the foal's level of readiness.

Approach the unhaltered foal and stroke and scratch and, if appearing calm and accepting, press its buttons. (See diagram on page 46). The cinch area, the gaskin area and the tail seat are ticklish areas we call "buttons" you should be able to stroke and touch these areas without jumpiness, bolting, kicking or biting as a response. If your foal passes the test you may repeat the harnessing exercise.

If your foal does not pass you must return to the "roping out" (or if you prefer you may use the "hosing out" procedure).

> **Sidebar -**
> ## The Difficult Ones.
> Every animal is different. Some respond <u>very</u> fast to the training, others seem to take longer. If your animal seems to be unreceptive to the exercises the approach I recommend is to make the lessons shorter, denser, and repeat, repeat, and repeat. Then go away for 3 or 4 days and return. You might be surprised with what you discover. Ninety-five percent of the time the more difficult to train animal has the greatest potential to become a superior workhorse.

Jess Ross (right) and I (left) watch as a young horse moves freely around the round pen with harness on. The trainers need to be just as attentive, curious, and courageous as they ask their trainee horses to be. And by courageous I mean willing to trust their instincts about how far to go with an individual animal.

Although most of the foundation training procedures can be handled easily by one person, having another person along to help is sure a blessing. It always seems to me that when Jess and I work together we're able to see and react to about three times as much information and circumstance as I can alone.

But of course some people are better off alone. And it can be hard to find the right combination of temperments, working styles, and values in two people. It's sort of like putting together a good team of horses. I know I'm fortunate to have Jess as a friend and co-worker in the training.

With the foal harnessed, a bit fastened in the halter, and lines attached, pull on one line as the animal stands. Wait until the foal gives a little to the pressure and give the customary command to go. Immediately be prepared to apply pressure to the opposite line: Apply pressure, don't pull on it. What you want to do is avoid having the foal turn 180 degrees to face you. But if this happens don't fret. *(Actually you may be pleased if it does turn to face you because two things have happened. The foal has yielded to the bit pressure and turned, and the foal is looking to you for help. Big success with both indications).*

Now if it did come full around, gently push the foal's head away and say WHOA. You want to pass behind the foal and repeat the exercise but in the other direction. After that get the foal to move ahead of you along the wall of the round pen and don't worry about turns. You just want to move ahead. When things are moving smoothly stop and reward the foal. Now start again and this time as the foal moves ahead, apply some pressure to the line that's on the inside of the round pen but do not slack on the other line, just prepare to give a little when the foal begins to turn. Take any turn as a success. You want to make a complete turn and be heading around the pen in the opposite direction.

For the next step you should have someone available to help.

Tie a rope at least 15' long, to the center of a single tree. Hook the single tree to the last link of the traces on the trainee's harness (See ***Betsy's Secondary Training*** photos in the next chapter). Your helper (with gloves on), needs to hold the rope taught so that the single tree rises off the ground. Now start your horse and repeat previous exercises. Doing this now gives the foal a little something extra to think about and seems to relax resistance to turns. If your trainee moves comfortably allow the single tree to drag on the ground but keep hold of the rope. Have your helper raise and lower the single tree until the horse doesn't care about its being there. Also have your helper pull back hard on the rope as the foal walks ahead. This puts pressure on the shoulders and prepares the foal for pulling.

You will have to use common sense to decide if you need to cut the lessons into shorter sessions given more often, or if you may combine lessons and speed up the process. Experience has shown that, in the beginning, you do not want to have lessons go beyond 30 minutes without at least a 2 hour break. The risk is that the attentive, curious, concerned trainee will become angry, sullen, and resistant thereby reducing or eliminating the effectiveness of the lesson.

You can use these lessons with any animal from 4 to 18 mos. of age with special variations applicable if the animal has suffered abuse at the hand of a human. Those variations are covered indirectly in the chapter on correcting problems.

Accomplishments:

1. complete foundation training including:

> full acceptance
>
> good behavior
>
> manageability

2. courage aided

3. harness and driving well started

The lessons that would result in advanced driving, hitching and actual work are identical to those covered in the next two age groups and are outlined in the next three chapters.

138

Chapter Ten

Training Two and Three Year Olds

With this age group there may be one major difference from the routine just outlined in Chapter Nine. And this difference is certainly tied to the individual animal's personality and experience level. If this youngster has never been handled much, and definitely never mistreated, its acceptance of you, as a result of the round pen work, might be startlingly quick.

If, on the other hand, this youngster has painful, fearful, or pranksterish memories of people you may find it takes quite a bit of patience to gain acceptance as the dominate partner in a working relationship.

These are, by no means, the sum total of what you might expect. Expect the unexpected and you will often be closer to what really happens. (Also recall the comments from the previous chapters about the correlation between superior individual equine intelligence and training difficulty with that animal. It will be up to you whether or not that animal will end up as a working partner or an outlaw.)

I have had " green" three year olds accept the halter AND THE HARNESS within 20 minutes! It can happen that quick, but I do not recommend that you push for such a goal because, if you can't "read" the animal's signals clearly you may do more harm than good. And because the repetition of the early lessons will build a solid foundation, something you don't want to be without.

The way you will start out with a two or three year old will be basically the same, regardless of its previous handling, as the round pen approach outlined in the previous chapter with this subtle difference: When working the animal back and forth look for early signs of acceptance. As soon as it turns to face you (perhaps even bobbing its head a little) approach calmly and go directly to the side to pet and lightly scratch the withers. Be "matter-of-fact". If, as you approach, the animal moves away from you say WHOA immediately. If it does not stop and stand, accept that as a clear indication that you must return to the very beginnings of the round pen routine. Push the horse away from you with a "Giddup" command and block its path, stopping it with a simultaneous WHOA command. Always watch for that little sign of acceptance and be prepared to walk through that door. I hope the photos which follow will further illustrate the procedure and go on to demonstrate how important and efffective this beginning is to the next stages of training.

When you gain this acceptance be ready to return with halter and rope. Slip the rope around the neck carefully. My suggestion is to lay it across the lower neck just above the withers. Now work it up the neck to behind the ears. Next with the same approach used in Chapter Nine, halter the horse. But in this case you can and should expect a quiet, willing, "accepting" horse. If it tries to get away return to the "acceptance training' routine.

The horse that is willing to stand quietly (perhaps with a little apprehension - but quietly) to be haltered for the first time is demonstrating tremendous acceptance and courage. Try to imagine the roles reversed and think what it might take for you to allow some other beast to put a bunch of straps around your head and neck! This lesson in empathy is important because it can illustrate just how casual and uncaring we can let ourselves become with horses.

I have done this acceptance training routine with more horses than I can count yet it still floods me with wonder and appreciation for this marvelous creature. And those two emotions are communicated to the horses and provide glue to hold our future relationships together.

The goals and reasonable accomplishments for this age group are the same as Chapter Nine.

The photo series which follow are of two of our two year olds (at the time of this writing). One of them you met in the last chapter as a weanling, Betsy. The other is her 3/4 brother, Ted. Although they were out of sisters and the same stallion, Abe, and born a week apart you may notice that there is substantial size difference. Ted is a monstrously big two year old with a sweet disposition but he does not demonstrate the curious nature and intelligence of his sister Betsy. As with Betsy, Ted was not imprinted but he was halter trained as a nursing foal. Ted was gelded as a weanling and turned out with his sister to pasture. He did not go through the same inital acceptance training as demonstrated in the Betsy photos from the last chapter. Over eighteen months later we returned to both foals, now two year olds, to determine what they retained. Notice in these photos the subtle, but important, differences in how they react to the same routines. Their reactions and my instincts are what lead me to the assessment of the relative intelligences.

Sidebar: Trust from Work

Many people and horses arrive at a point of trust without conscious effort - more as the result of long hours of team work out of practical necessity. For example: You cannot sucessfully work horses for 100 or 200 days of the year without the routine beginning to affect your posture and attitude - as well as the horses. Most people do not think about affecting a change in the attitude - and becoming more tolerant of the horse - in order to become more successful. They just set out to get their work done. But often this change is the very result of long hours of shared work. It should be said, however, that there are those few people and horses who cannot be helped through hard work.

Acceptance Training: Ted

A. Ted moves away from me freely but...

B. ... to even my surprise he's only been through the 'back and forth' just once when he stops, turns to me and approaches bobbing his head.

C. As I approach him he starts to back away and I stop, thinking I'll let him go through the routine again...

D.(Above) He turns and comes to me. Full acceptance. I go and get the halter and lead rope while he stands still.

E. (Far Left) He calmly allows me to put a lead rope across his withers and rub up and down his neck. I'm six foot tall without my hat so you can see how big this two year old is!

F. (Left) I spread the basket of the halter out and ...

141

F. I reach over his neck and get ahold of the halter's poll strap and pull the basket over his nose.

H. And finally I buckle the halter. Please note the posture of this young horse. He's perfectly calm, ears at attention, not the least bit concerned about what I'm doing but wide awake to the world around him. He's accepted me as his dominate partner without restraint or pain or hassle. This entire exercise took less than 10 minutes. Concerned that perhaps it went too easy, I ask Jess Ross to immediately take over the next business with Ted.

142

Roping Out: Ted

A. We take the halter off Ted and Jess approaches with the long lariat and puts the loop over his head. Ted starts to walk away.

B. Jess maintains a slack rope and backs to the center of the pen preparing to swing the lariat like it was a jump rope.

C. Ted runs to the opposite side of the pen and steps over the swinging rope as he does so. Jess says WHOA, no pressure on the rope, and Ted stops.

D. Now Jess starts flipping the rope around and gives Ted the command to go.

E. The rope keeps getting flipped all over Ted's moving body with no let up.

F. Although Ted's moving out he's not showing any signs of real panic.

G. But its important for Jess to keep at it with the flipping, snaking lariat.

H. And here we begin to see the very first signs of a particular kind of relaxation on the young gelding's part. Jess prepares himself to say WHOA simultaneous with Ted's voluntary stop.

I. Ted stops and stands still while Jess keeps flipping the rope. At this point we're looking for the next signs of acceptance. We want Ted to voluntarily turn and face us.

This is Ted's first experience with the roping out so we aren't concerned about some of the specifics you'll see in Betsy's next series. It's just important that he be given the opportunity to get used to the ever present flipping rope. Some say this desensitizes the horse. I don't agree, I feel it gives them a sense of courage to deal with that which might ordinarily cause them to flee.

J. Ted turns to face and accept Jess and the rope. A major turning point in this good young gelding's life as a work horse. And done so easily and without risk.

K. But Jess needs to know the acceptance is total and genuine. He approaches Ted with the coils of rope in hand and talks and touches him reassuringly. Ted rewards Jess by standing absolutely still and paying complete attention.

L. Jess gathers up a mess of the lariat coils and casually rubs them all over Ted who stands perfectly still. Next Jess puts the rope around Ted's pasterns and lifts his feet as was explained at the end of the previous chapter. (The Betsy photos which follow illustrate this well.)

145

M & N. To finish off this roping out session I remove the lariat from Ted's hind leg and pick the leg up. He offers no resistance and as you can see he is not tied up or restrained. He's ready for the second roping out session and then harnessing and driving.

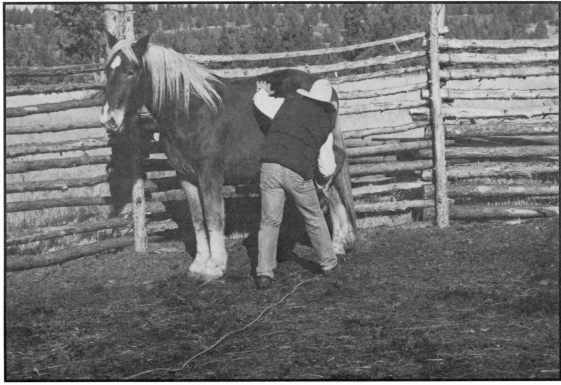

Roping Out and Beyond: Betsys' Secondary Training

A. Yes, this is the same filly from the last chapter only at the time of this photo she's two years old. Remember she's been through all this before, but it was quite a while ago and we aren't sure how much she's retained. So Jess pushes her away with a command to go.

B. And she moves away very nicely.

D. After a couple of rounds with two WHOAS she turns to face Jess and he approaches her.

C. It's interesting to see how free she moves and how calm she is. Also she's leaning into her turn and following her head, indications that she will probably do nicely when the driving commences.

E. Jess goes back to the fence and gets a lead rope and returns to Betsy. We want to see how she reacts to this thing in his hand. She pays excellent attention but it doesn't break her "acceptance" of Jess. All of this has taken less than five minutes.

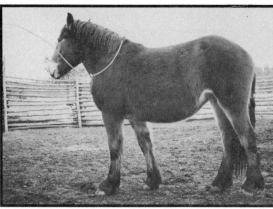

F. As Jess leaves Betsy she follows him with her eyes, still paying attention, still connected, still in "acceptance".

G. Since Jess was so readily accepted by Betsy we decided that I would do the roping out. So I put the loop around her patient head and start in with a "jump rope" swirl.

H. And she just looks at me, even when I flip the rope over her back and under her tail. She is ready, very ready.

I. So I pass the rope under her belly and slowly pull the slack out as she casually walks around.

J. In this closeup you can see that the rope is an intrusion, a nuisance, but not hurtful.

K. When the slack was pretty much out I swirled the rope and it bumped her hocks and slapped her butt.

L. From behind I pitch some slack and begin swinging the rope back and forth as I follow her.

M. Big moment...I ask her to stop and she does, while I continue to swing the rope from one hock to the other. She stands in total acceptance.

N. I go to her with the rope in hand, pull some slack up over her back, this time I pass from behind and between the pen fence and her. She stands totally compliant, unafraid, curious, attentive.

O. I pick up the loose end of the rope and pull it between her front legs. She watches the rope closely but does not move. She's ready for the foot work.

P. I lay out a loop in the lariat and run my hand down the leg and pick it up. Betsy is not tied up or restrained in any way. She can walk away if she wishes.

Q. Holding the leg I slip the rope over the pastern.

R. Here Jess takes over and gently pulls up Betsy's leg. She offered a little resistance and then actually held her leg up so that there was little pressure on the rope.

S. Here's another angle shot showing the leg held up from opposite side and rope under the belly. Again look at Betsy's demeanor. She is fully accepting of this routine.

T. In this shot you can see Betsy displaying a little annoyance with the set of her ears. Yet even with this, you can clearly see that she is holding her own leg up.

U.& V. Jess has taken the lariat away and returned to Betsy to pickup each foot. Now is the time to reinforce that the rope is an extension and unneccesary. We want her to know we are to be allowed to pick up her feet. We quit at this point, feeling we had tremendous success and not wanting to annoy her further. We turned her out in a large dry lot with Ted and other trainees for hay and relaxation.

151

W. The very next day John and Twinka Lupher came out to see if they wanted to purchase Betsy. The photos on this page and the next were taken by Twinka Lupher. In this photo I have Betsy in the round pen and I have gone to her to "press her buttons" to see if she's retained the same level of acceptance as she had the day before with the roping out routine. Here John Lupher watches as I pinch Betsy under the belly where a cinch might ride. She doesn't care.

X. Here I am pressing another button and she doesn't care. Notice she is not restrained.

Y. Jess has then haltered Betsy and introduced her to the collar. She accepts harnessing without being tied up. We hang a bit in her halter and drive her for the first time around the round pen. She does so well that we go immediately to the next step...

Z. Here we have fastened a single tree to Betsy's tugs and I hold a long soft rope that is, in turn, fastened to the single tree. Jess is poised with a whip to make sure that Betsy steps ahead on command to go. This is important because my little pressure on the rope translates to an unfamiliar weight on her shoulders. She must not refuse to move, at this point. She did very well and the Luphers became her new owners.

153

Joyce Sharp raking hay on Singing Horse Ranch

John Male driving four abreast on a disc in Ontario, Canada

Chapter Eleven

Starting and Training Older Horses
(Four years and on)

Some may wonder at my choosing to include in a group called "older horses," four year olds. (For those of you who may not know, four year old horses are generally considered young.) The reason I include them is that the routine I use for 18 year old horses is the same as what I use for 4 or 5 year olds. What I find in common throughout this large age group catagory is that they are all mature enough to behave similarly in training situations. In fact let me go so far to say I have found age (and advanced age) not to be a detriment to learning in horses. About ten years ago I had occasion to train a 30 year old mare to skid light logs. She did exceedingly well.

There is a long standing western tradition to leave horses alone until they are four or five years old and then "break" them for work. The rationale is that you don't work them hard until that age so why mess with them before then? There is also, I'm sure, another very real and perhaps practical reason. As I said many pages ago, the easiest horse to train is the five year old which has had little or no human contact. And it is dramatically so. We have no concrete evidence to tell us why this is the case. We can only imagine what might change in a horse's psyche as it leaves its foalhood and heads into adulthood.

All that said I still prefer to start horses young and bring them along gradually in the work routine. It results in such superior animals. However, we maintain a horse herd of 30 to 50 head of varying ages. That results in a tight schedule and often doesn't allow best intentions to bloom. For us it is more common to "imprint" the foal and gain total acceptance and turn it out, returning occasionally for hoof care, vet treatments, and worming, but not to commence with full harness training until three to five years old. Again this is not a preference' it's a reality.

We use the acceptance training routine, in the round pen, (see chapters nine and ten) with older horses regardless of their previous handling by humans. If we have a horse with severe behavior problems or psychosis we use the same routine but may customize some of the specific timing and approaches. Specific corrective variables are covered in Chapter

155

Thirteen, but the story of Juniper (which follows) and the photos of her sessions should illustrate my contention that the best approach to most behavior problems in horses is to return to the basic foundation training and work up from there.

People who have watched me work a foal in the round pen with some success have commented that this was great but they were sure it wouldn't work so well with a full-sized draft horse. Actually, as you will discover with the following pictures, it works better. At the risk of redundancy in the pictorials, I'm including in this chapter a complete training routine with one young mare and part of the routine with a young gelding. I want you to see different reactions and how they might be handled.

About five years ago an older teamster gentlemen watched as I worked a 7 year old gelding in the round pen. The gelding was totally green and I put him through the acceptance training routine. This horse caught on so quick that within one half hour I went from him being afraid of me to his being harnessed and ground driven. I quit at that point and unharnessed the gelding. As I carried the harness back to the barn I overheard this gentleman, who was walking away and shaking his head. He mumbled loud "Voodoo, voodoo or drugs, one or the other...anyway it ain't right, it ain't right." He got in his pickup and drove off. I'm sharing this reaction with you now because what you are about to see in the following series, entitled "June's Training", may also seem either unbelievable or unremarkable. Unbelieveable because your own experience with horses may be so different, and perhaps difficult, that you find it hard to believe it can work this way. Or unremarkable because some of you may think that this young mare was trained before these photos were taken. I tell you now that it does work this way and it works extremely well. And I also tell you that this mare was not trained to harness or drive before these photos were taken. In fact she came with some definite emotional baggage. You are seeing the actual training session. It isn't voodoo and it is right, the system works to the advantage of the horse and the person.

This routine, which provides us with our foundation training, does not include the hitching and actual working. Those procedures follow in the next chapter. And those procedures are made easy and comfortable by this preliminary work.

The mare featured in this first series of photos is Juniper. She is a four year old out of our excellent furrow mare Lana and our stallion Abe. Her history to the point of this training exercise is important and points up how many variables are possible in each individual horse's psychological makeup. We were careful to have the right opportunity to record her training session in photographs because of what we know about her. She was imprinted at birth and halter trained. When she was one month old and still nursing she developed a serious navel-ill condition which required that we doctor her several times a day. The doctoring required that we insert a medicated cauterizing stick up into her navel cavity. This hurt. Before long she feared our coming. And after a bit she seemed to get downright mad. (I would too in the same situation.) We healed her up and saved her life (thanks to our exceptional veterinarian, Eric Sharpnack).

As a big weanling she encountered a porcupine which covered her nose, lips and roof of her mouth with quills. We restrained her and got the quills out. After that she became quite difficult to catch. When she was a yearling, in my absense our excellent farrier mistook her for another filly ("all those sorrel Belgians look alike!") and set to working on her feet. I don't know what exactly occurred but she tried to kick and bite him, and succeeded in ending the session on her terms. All of these experiences, and perhaps a few I don't know about, went into the mix to make of her an angry young mare with little tolerance of people and being handled. I elected, early on, to let her grow up to a serviceable age before taking a training routine to her. One reason was that I figured time and maturity would aid me in my job. And I knew that she would benefit from being able to go into a regular work schedule. And I confess to the less than honorable plan that I would save her for a dramatic series of photos for this book. Jess and I frequently commented on how we expected that she would be a real handful. She acted like a mare who would runaway for one of the worst reasons - determined cussedness. The horse that runs away because of fear is often retrainable. The horse that runs away because it is fed up with the routine is hard to deal with. We knew she was intelligent, prone to meanness, and hypersensitive to anything around her belly and face. Jess said, "It'll be good to show people that some horses are difficult or impossible to work with." It is an understatement to say that we , Jess and I, were very surprised by the results of that first session but we kept expecting her to blow up. I'll let the series of photos tell you the rest of the story.

Starting: Juniper's Training

A. Remember that we are expecting trouble with this mare (or filly if your prefer), I know from experience that I can catch her if I corner her but that is not acceptable to me. She doesn't let me get too close before she moves out. I'm quick to give a go command.

B. It is very important that she get the impression that she's moving only because I want her to. It might not seem like an important distinction whether she's trying to get away or perceives I'm pushing her away - BUT IT IS IMPORTANT if we are to win acceptance.

157

C. A couple of times back and forth and she's quickly picking up on my position relative to her's. She's watching me real close.

D. When I get to that check-mate position across from her eyes, where the intelligent mare clearly perceives that soon I will be able to cross her path, she stops and I say WHOA. She doesn't trust me and I can read that in her posture.

E. As she turns her head to face me, experience has taught that her's is an intelligent, even clever, attitude. The horse with this nature, coupled to a series of bad experiences, will resort to violence if cornered or forced into something. It may not be obvious but this mare is on the edge, her life could go quite easily to an outlaw nature. And that would be a tragedy because she is a lovely creature of high intelligence and a candidate to make an exceptional workmate. I even have my eye on her for "leader" potential. I start her up again, and take her back and forth a couple of more times, not forgetting to offer her opportunities to go her way, and always leaving open the route direct to me.

F. Notice that throughout I've maintained my distance from her, trying to avoid letting her feel trapped. And in this frame we see the reward. After just about five minutes she starts to turn towards me. The subtle difference between this photo and the previous one should be studied. Something of the young mare's dominate attitude is gone in this posture. I'm surprised because I also recognize that she's thinking real hard about me, not about available routes of escape. I'm certain that she can't respond this quickly to the acceptance training, so I expect her to approach a little and then make a break to get away.

G. But she surprises me completely.

H. These exceptional photos show her total and complete acceptance of me.

I. She walks freely to me, relaxed yet attentive.

J. I take one step forward to meet her, an important gesture of reciprocal acceptance, and stroke her face.

K. I walk around to her left side.

L. And go to her neck and withers. At this point, short though the lesson is, I figure maybe it would be good to end it here...

M. But again she surprises me. As I walk away, I stoop down to pickup the halter I dropped and proceed as though to leave the pen. Juniper follows me.

N. I look over and notice that she seems to be saying "don't go."

O. I stop and turn around to visit with her and am surprised to see her complete acceptance of the halter as well as myself. This is not the same mare! What a transformation.

P. I hold the halter out and she puts her nose into it!

Q. & R. She is so willing and receptive to this process that I make the decision to go on to step two. I go and fetch the snaps and bit.

Bitting: Juniper's Training

A.This is still the same session. I return to Juniper with a snaffle bit and two double snaps. Notice her manner and posture! I snap on the lead rope.

B. I let the lead rope hang free, I want her used to standing quietly with the rope hanging below her chin. I snap the bit into the halter hardware.

C. Here you can see the bit as I position it to put in her mouth. Juniper has never had a bit in her mouth before now.

D. I pull the bit through and snap it to the opposite side.

E. With the bit in place I tighten the halter poll strap so that the bit fits better. Notice that she is not tied or restrained in any way. She's accepted the bitting beautifully. And I'll leave it in her mouth for about a half hour. This seems long enough to let them just start to get used to the sensation. Bitting the horse before you harness and teach to drive allows that there will be one less intrusion or surprise for the trainee to deal with.

Even after all these years I am still amazed at how well this approach works. And these sessions with Juniper just adds to that feeling.

You can whisper to them, you can touch them, and they will move for you.
But first you must communicate your place and role in their world.

Earning a willing compliance rather than extricating submission results in a far superior work mate.

With horses acceptance changes the character of reaction.

I wrote earlier that Juniper had problems with people handling her feet. Seeing as she had such an incredible transformation in attitude, Jess and I decided to see how she would respond, at the tail end of the first session, if I picked up her foot. To make sure we didn't loose ground I asked Jess to hold her lead rope as I lifted her foot . Her ears came back and she wasn't happy but she did allow me to pickup and hold up her foot. Tremendous change. We decide her first session is done and turn her loose.

At the end of that first session we were flabbergasted at the change in Juniper and her overall receptiveness to the way we handled her. But we also still remember the old her and were expecting trouble. Although it is good to be cautious and sensible, in a way I was making a mistake with my prejudices. She was showing me respect, trust, and acceptance and what was I showing in return? Scepticism, distrust, surprise? In hindsight, and with the benefit of these photos to review, I feel that what little problems we had, and they were very little, might have been avoided altogether had I shown her all that she had shown me.

The next day we returned to her with the roping out exercise in mind.

Roping Out: Juniper's Training

A. The very next day I take Juniper back into the round pen and approach her with the coils of the 65 foot lariat.

B. In the beginning she seems pretty trusting but as I rub it over her body she starts to get angry. Yet she still stands still.

162

B.& C. So I keep at it putting, the rope back and forth over her head and over her back.

D. And I notice a growing change in her manner. She's not afraid, but neither is she willing to just stand for this. She's losing her patience.

E. She finally decides she wants to leave.

F. So I throw the loop over her head and she turns around...

G. ...which causes the rope to go around her girth. I like that because, for what has to happen, I don't care where the rope is.

H. With the rope slack I flip it around on the ground as she runs around the pen. I don't quit when she stops, I just keep flipping the rope. When she turns towards me I go to her, pet her and move the rope to a different position.

I. I get her going again and work her back and forth. Her haste and anxiety is just about gone.

J. She has stopped on my command and stands still while I whirl the rope which is around one back leg.

K. I go to her with praise and as I return to walk back to the rope I sense her starting to move. I turn and say WHOA and she looks at me as if to say "I was only kidding"

L. & M. From the center of the pen I use the rope's position to raise and lower her leg.

N. I go to her to reassure her and she's glad for that but still anxious about the rope.

O. So I pull it out full length between her front legs. Then I make a coil in the end of the rope and pull it towards her slowly and then in jerks.

P. She watches the rope come towards her and listens to my reassurances.

Q. In this situation the natural reaction of a horse is to run away. Juniper is not restrained, she could leave.

R. As the little knot in the end of the lariat approaches her legs, she sniffs it. Tremendous courage and intelligence are being demonstrated here.

S. And finally she says "so what?" I'm well pleased with this fifteen minute session and call it a day.

Harnessing: Juniper's Training

A. We decide Juniper needs a different person to work with so Jess takes this session. A couple of pushes and whoas and she comes to Jess for haltering.

B. Haltered and with lead rope hanging free Juniper sniffs the collar Jess brings over. She's never seen one before.

C. There's nothing holding Juniper where she is as Jess puts the collar on her. She's perfectly calm.

D. I like this picture! Juniper stands still as Jess drags a mean old mess of never-seen-before harness, with jingling chains. Hard to believe she's never been harnessed before.

E. Jess goes to Juniper and offers to let her sniff and look at the harness, close-up. She appears to be disinterested.

F. When Jess goes to lift the harness on Juniper she reverts back to old form and decides she doesn't like the idea...

G. ..but she's moving slow and Jess stays with her, so she only takes two steps before stopping on command.

H. As Jess gets the harness centered on her, she gives a pose that says she's totally accepted the routine. "Go ahead, it's okay", she seems to be saying.

I. Jess gets the hames in the collar grooves.

J. And moves around to center them for proper draft.

K. He decides to pass under her neck to see if she's still tolerant and she most definitely is. (Notice that Jess has centered the harness on the back so that it should not fall off either side or back and startle her.)

L. The hame strap gets fastened tightly.

M. And Juniper gives a little surprise side step as Jess pulls the brichen down.

N. Jess carefully reads her manner before crossing behind.

O. Juniper and Jess reassure each other.

P. Juniper is perfectly comfortable with Jess reaching under her belly to fasten the quarter straps.

Q. Hooking the breast strap.

R. Jess finishes up the harnessing by fastening the belly band. Next he'll take the lead rope off and leave Juniper alone in harness.

S. She wanders around the pen getting used to the straps and chains bouncing.

T. She moves into a nice casual gait.

U. Until finally she is accepting and has calmed herself about the harness.

You notice in all the photo series we offered covering the harnessing process that the horses are standing, untied, with lead rope hanging. Please keep in mind that these horses are standing in a closed round pen and MOST IMPORTANT they have each been put through the acceptance training including the roping out. Their foundation training, up to the moment of harnessing, is the reason they are so accepting of this process. If you go for short cuts and do not do this complete process, an attempt to harness a green horse that is unrestrained will result in a strong reaction and possibly a horse in flight from fright. Also, if you tie up a horse in a less than secure fashion and it goes into a panic during harnessing, you could end up with a dangerous situation as the horse tears up whatever it is fastened to.

We leave our horses unrestrained during harnessing because we are training them to stand when we wish, regardless of what is happening around and to them. This will be important, later, when we need them to do the same thing hitched to a vehicle or implement.

Driving: Juniper's Training

A. At the same session as the harnessing we, after Juniper is accustomed to her harness, snap a bit back into her halter and buckle single lines on.

B. As I give the first command to go you can see Juniper trying to figure out the pressure on that bit in her mouth.

C. Then Juniper reverts and seems to say "let me out of here." Which is fine because we just go round and round in the pen with me trying to convince her, once again, that her forward motion is my wish.

D. By staying towards the center of the pen my circles are smaller and I don't need to travel at nearly the speed Juniper chooses. I work to be matter of fact about how it all is going. Nothing bad can happen.

E. & F. Here I can see and feel a change in her manner as she slows and begins to accept the process.

G. Juniper stopped on her own and I said Whoa at that same instant. Then she turned 180 degrees and set off again with me following.

H. As she slowed naturally I applied a very slight pressure on the lines and said a sharp WHOA. And she stopped nicely.

I. So I went to her and thanked her for her amazing cooperation. You can see how all that roping out has paid off.

J. We go around a couple more times at a walk and I force her to turn across the pen.

K. Midway across I set her head to make a U turn careful to be prepared to move quickly to stay behind her.

L. In this closeup you can see how she is resisting the bit's position, a natural early reaction that requires a firm but compassionate perserverance on the teamster's half.

M. Making a turn requires that you maintain nearly equal tension on both driving lines, it's just that the line on the inside of the turn is a bit shorter and creates an angle to the bit in the horse's mouth.

N. The mare then turns her head to make the bit position in her mouth straight and therefore more comfortable. Next the body follows the head.

O. Juniper stops on my command and seems attentive yet relaxed.

P. I go to her with my full and genuine gratitude.

Q. We make a few more rounds and with each pass she gets more comfortable and casual.

R. We end this 45 minute session thrilled and a bit tired.

Finishing Juniper's Schooling

With Juniper's next routine we will hook a single tree on with a rope as we did for Betsy last chapter. If she accepts it well we will fasten a fence post to the single tree and drive her around the round pen for fifteen minutes to half an hour.

After this we will return with her harnessed in the round pen and put on a bridle with blinders and repeat some earlier exercises.

After this we will take her out of the round pen and hook her with a quiet well broke horse to the wagon or forecart and drive her for two or three one hour trips. Next this we will hook her to some farm implements and put her to work. We expect no problems and are reinforced in our belief that the foundation training of the round pen is going to turn out another excellent work mate.

(The routines outlined above are covered in detail in the next chapter.)

The Well Started Horse

The next photo series deals with Juniper's three quarter brother "Thom". I am hoping that by describing something of Thom's experience and background and taking you through his initial driving introduction you will be able to discern how you might customize an approach for your own well started horse.

I am often asked if it is difficult to train a broke saddle horse to work in harness. I can't give a helpful precise answer because there are two many variables. If your horse will stand quietly, accept your work around him, stop on command, go on command, and so forth - yes, you can get them working very quickly. But many so-called broke saddle horses are just barely so.

Thom is four years old. He is out of our best work mare, Cali, and by Abe. Cali is Lana's sister. Thom was imprinted, fully halter trained and subjected to the "day care center" when mom went to work. Thom has had his feet worked on from six months old. To my knowledge Thom has never had anything go wrong in his young life. We intended to try to team Thom up with his sister Juniper. We may still. It depends on how they walk and work together.

On the same days when we started Juniper we took Thom into the round pen twice. The first time we put him through a quick acceptance routine and a very short roping out. These were condensed lessons because it was obvious he didn't seem to need them. The harnessing photos which appeared in chapter four are of Thom's first experience. As you can see, he did amazingly well. This is the value of all that early work. One observer said of Thom "he was born broke!" Not so, Thom is the result of good training and handling, as much as breeding. And he is always a pure pleasure to be around.

The photos which follow are of Thom's second experience which included his first time driving.

174

The Well Started Horse: Thom's Training

A. Thom stands in the middle of the round pen with halter and loose lead rope. I've put his collar on and come back with the harness. He's calm and attentive.

B. I slide the harness up just behind the collar and set the far hame over Thom's withers.

C. Here I'm spreading the harness out evenly over his middle back. Notice his manner.

D. As I balance out the harness he looks as though he's falling asleep. I actually prefer a little anxiety to sleepiness because the alert, curious, cautious horse is less likely to be surprised and jump.

E. & F. No part of the harnessing process seems to bother him. This is further evidence of the great value of foundation training.

G. & H. In these two photos Thom shows more curiousity and attention as I finish up the harnessing. I like the fact that he's looking around and seems to be thinking, yet he stays put as I work. Can't ask for more!

I. Done with the harnessing I walk away and leave Thom to consider his new suit of work clothes.

J. He does not move until I push him when he shows a fine willing form as he steps out.

K. He seems the slightest bit annoyed as he trots around the pen for two rounds.

L. And then his manner changes and he slows to a comfortable walk, ears sharp and fully attentive.

M. Then Thom cuts across the pen and comes looking for me. He seems to be asking if I might help him with his confusion.

N. Thom has demonstrated such a quick acceptance of everything we've brought to him that I elect to go straight to the blindered bridle for his first driving lessons. Using the same approach as illustrated with Juniper, I push Thom ahead and let him move at his pace. He can't get away or hurt himself in this round pen so I let him sort out the experience and choose the path of greatest comfort - all on his own. Even so I am there to cleverly claim credit for whenever he chooses to go or stop or turn.

O. Within five minutes we are stopping on command and working on our turns. Notice the slack in the lines: I most definitely do not want to abuse the mouth of the trainee. I am working from here on out to have a sensitive mouth that will allow me the widest range of signals. I want to be able to apply a little pressure on one line and get a smooth gradual turn. I want to be able to pull back slightly and have the horse(s) slow down. I want to be able to "steer" my horse(s) in a perfectly straight line. All those things start here with the right bit/line pressure.

P. Thom has gone through this fifteen minute driving session in outstanding form. He became a little stubborn about starting and I tapped him with a light driving whip. Even with that he gets an A+.

The next routine for Thom will be to drag the single tree. After that we'll drag a fence post hitched to the single tree. All this happens in the round pen. We are working on his stops, turns and starts. When he has successfully completed this routine we will take him outside and hitch him to the wagon or forecart, with a quiet broke horse, for a few extended cross-country drives. Depending on his progress, and our designs for his future, we may hitch him with another trainee - or with a broke horse - or perhaps in a larger hitch. If we are looking for a quick road to a finished well broke horse we will make sure to put Thom into a routine of regular field work for at least a month. If we do not have work for him right away we aren't concerned because experience has shown he will retain 99% of what he's learned.

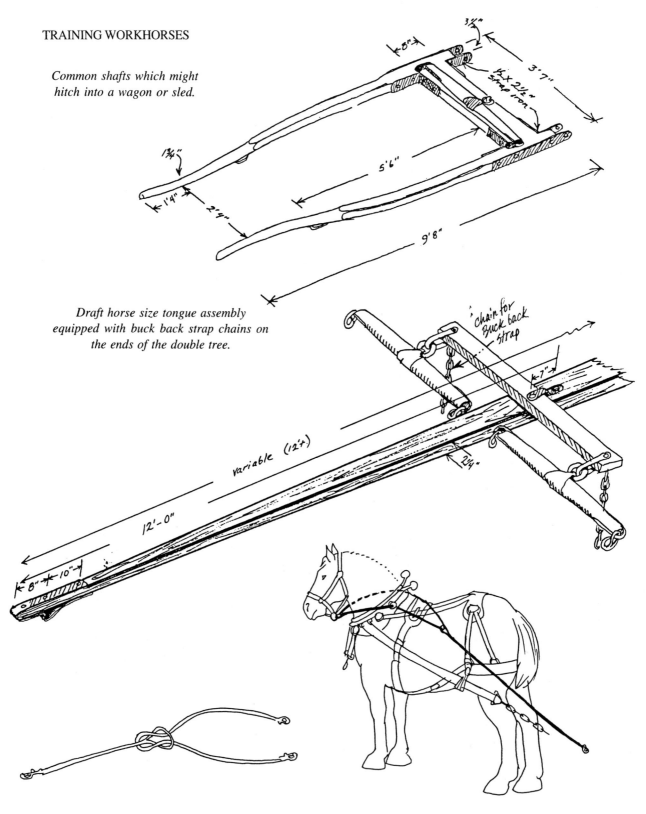

*Common shafts which might
hitch into a wagon or sled.*

8"

3½"

3'·7"

½ x 2½"
strap iron

1¾"

1'4"

2'4"

5'6"

9'8"

*Draft horse size tongue assembly
equipped with buck back strap chains on
the ends of the double tree.*

chain for
Buck back
strap

7"

variable (12'+)

2'4"

12'-0"

8" 10"

Buck Back Strap

Buck Back Strap on horse

178

Chapter Twelve

Follow Through to Finish

A Working Routine

Well, in case you haven't picked up on it by now I guess I'll just come out with it. I believe that the most important portion of a successful training program for workhorses has already been outlined and demonstrated. Everything you've read and looked at, up to this point, fits into what I call "foundation". What comes after is what I call "finish". I don't mean to suggest that what follows is easy, in many cases it requires greater skill from the trainer. But I am saying that the trainer's job is MADE easier by a complete and solid foundation. And I am saying that what we call "foundation" work is MORE important than finish though it might actually be easier to realize.

This might sound like an afterword to all the material we just went through but I need to comment on the important advantages this foundation work provides. Before we ever hook a horse to a vehicle or implement, with the mutual acceptance foundation work we have trainees which are;

1. easy to catch and halter
2. easy to lead
3. easy to trim and/or shoe
4. broke to stand quietly (untied)
5. well mannered in a tie stall
6. willing to go on voice command
7. willing to back on voice command
8. willing to stop on voice command
9. easy to harness and bridle
10. schooled to ground drive
11. willing to pull a light load
12. unafraid of something dragging behind
13. courageous /self confident
14. interested in work
15. accepting of us
16. trusting us

Some experienced teamsters will be quick to say that this checklist includes things that are all accomplished by work, long hours of actual work in harness. They believe that this is the only way to get to these stages with horses, stages they see as representing "finish" or "well-broke". While it is true that a solid working routine in the hands of a skilled and caring teamster WILL result in most or all of these things, I hope this book offers proof that you can accomplish this in early foundation training and that there is an advantage to doing it this way.

It is important to mention this because there are experienced teamsters who will fault the procedure we use for first-time hitching. They will say, and rightly so, that they cannot get away with such a casual light-duty process for the first times they hitch new work horses. I said "rightly so" because I hazard to presume that some of those worried experienced teamsters have seldom had an opportunity to "first-time hitch" a horse with the credentials of a solid foundation training. Far too many people tie-up (or tie-down) a screaming frightened green horse, throw harness on it and drag it (or trick it) into being hitched to a vehicle or apparatus of some sort. The horse is then turned loose and when it runs (notice I said when and not IF) paraphenalia is in place to trip or dump that horse on its knees and/or face. Repeats of this procedure often result in a horse forced to submit, with some predictability, to the working routine. I leave it to each of you to figure the relative value of the horse "broke" in this manner. Again I repeat what I said near the beginning of this book: I believe that the system or approach is not as important as the character and results of the individual trainer. If it seems like I'm contradicting myself, that's fine. Contradiction is closer to natural than any manmade absolutes, theoretical or otherwise.

We can, and do, use the first-time-hitching process outlined in this chapter BECAUSE the horses we bring to the process have only to pay attention to the hitching and then the phenomenon of forward, followed, movement. They don't have to worry about the restraints, the harness, the driving, our proximity and expectations. They are already used to all that stuff. So there's much less for them to have to think about. Therefore there's much less for them to fret over. Remember back to all that roping out and the free movement in harness? Those exercises were helping the trainee to deal with elements that would naturally panic them if forced upon horses without transition or explanation. We were training these horses to deal with panic. We were teaching our equine friends that we are trustworthy. We were welcoming their curiousity and involvement. We were respecting their part, present and future, in the relationship. We enjoy mutual acceptance with these young trainee workhorses.

One way you might describe this mutual acceptance training program is gradual. I don't mean it is necessarily slow. I mean we work to take the horse up through gradients of experience. And each gradient is important to the next. If we skip a lesson it can mean that acceptance of the next lesson will be more difficult. One of your challenges in designing your own training program will be to respect the nature of the animal while you balance your own level of experience. It is helpful to me to think about teamster experience in terms of a "vocabulary of response". Just as we might have immediate access to certain effective and comfortable words for communication (our vocabulary) we can and must develop automatic responses to certain teamster situations; responses which grant us the greatest opportunity for success and safety. We need, and thank heavens it naturally comes of experience and may be aided by education, to react in a split second to a teamster circumstance that may become good or bad. All of this is to say for the umpteenth time that the uneducated, unskilled, inexperienced teamster should not be training horses. And this definitely comes into play when we move into first time hitching and finishing of the trainee horses.

The way I will proceed with this chapter is deliberately backwards. I want first to talk about primary concern for the horse's mouth. Second I will cover exceptions to our working norm that may represent your circumstance. And then I will detail the preferred scenario. I ask that you read all the material before you attempt to do any of the exercises.

Protect The Horse's Mouth

Throughout the foundation training we worked to teach the horse to stop on voice command and kept bit pressure as a second line of communication. With these hitching and driving routines we will be verbally "asking" the horse to maintain the speeds we want and to stop and go. We will be taking every opportunity to be gentle with the horse's mouth. The reason is that we do not want to de-sensitize the mouth, or deaden it, through rough handling. We want it to stay as sensitive, as is natural, so that the slightest pressure communicates the desired message to the horse. If we are constantly yanking on the horse's mouth, or maintaining a hard line pressure, we will deny this sensitivity later. I feel that the best time to develop horses that drive well (up on the bit, heads up, into the collar, moving freely, responding immediately and accurately to signals) is from the beginning and throughout the training. And the first-time hitching is most definitely included.

For these reasons I prefer to do first-time hitching to wheeled vehicles rather than drags or sleds. When we are standing on sleds we risk having to lean back, or fall back, on the lines thereby abusing the horse's mouth. Also with a heavy sled or drag the anxious and willing horse might naturally want to go ahead quicker, feeling this might lessen the load. The result is often that a teamster feels he or she must "hold back" the horse(s) which of course means a constant tight line pressure which sets an abusive tone for the horse's mouth (and threatens to confuse the horse as to what is actually desired). I prefer to build the horse gradually to maximum pulling effort against the collar while always protecting the mouth, and starting with wheeled vehicles works well to this end.

We Only Have the One Horse?

As the preferred scenario involves at least two if not three horses I anticipate people coming up with this concerned reaction. Here are my recommendations of how you might proceed.

Return to the round pen with your horse harnessed and repeat the driving training with an emphasis on the verbal WHOA command performance. Repeat it over many times until your horse stops immediately on voice command. You may have to reinforce the lessons with line pressure but be prepared to back off and try stopping with little or no variation in the line pressure. Do this for three or four fifteen minutes sessions before you hook the single tree back on and drag a fence post around in the round pen. Repeat the stop and go procedures until your horse seems comfortable. Now put a five gallon can, or bigger, full of a few rocks, dead center in the round pen. With a blindered bridle on your trainee drag the fence post and drive your horse up to and past the can. When you yourself are even with the can kick it or rattle it somehow. Make sure your hands stay on the lines and that you are not in the path of the fence post. Your trainee may jump a little, a lot or not at all. If the horse does jump say Whoa and expect a stop. This is a test. If your horse fails it you must repeat it over and over again until it passes the test repeatedly. Keep the sessions at fifteen to thirty minutes maximum. After this, again with the post hooked to the single tree, start your horse and do a rapid repetition of the verbal command to go. This should result in the trainee picking up speed. You want a trot. Stay clear of the fence post. In the proper round pen environment, you and your horse are safe. Just as soon as your horse is in a trot say WHOA and be prepared to reinforce with suitable line pressure only IF it doesn't stop. If all the outlined training steps were completed the horse will stop. How quickly and comfortably it stops is very important to you now. What you are working towards is a trainee that will stop quickly no matter how much activity and confusion may be occuring to and around it.

Only when you are convinced this horse has learned its whoa lessons completely will you be prepared to leave the round pen. Ground drive, with nothing dragging behind, your trainee through the gate of the roundpen and into the great out of doors. Check to see how responsive he or she is to the line pressures and verbal commands. If all is good then attach the single tree and fence post and do some turns around a pasture or field with your trainee, testing responsiveness to commands. Immediately following a successful turn with the fence post dragging be prepared to hook your horse to the shafts of a two wheeled cart or light four wheeled wagon.

Preparations for hitching to cart: You MUST have someone to help you with this exercise and once again it should be someone who is knowledgeable and physically able. You need ample space to drive in with no hazards or extreme threats (i.e., cliffs, children's toys, barking dogs, electric fences, ferris wheels, screaming children, explosions, etc., etc.). You need a suitable vehicle. My first choice is a two wheeled implement forecart rigged with shafts. Second choice would be a two wheeled cart with a rear entry seat and a back foot board. Third choice would be a light low wagon rigged with shafts. You of course need suitable harness with shaft loops or some such accommodation and a suitable whip. If you do not know what

I'm talking about you can look it up in the **Work Horse Handbook.** But the complete truth is that if you don't know what this stuff is you should not be risking this procedure. An experienced teamster, dealing with a foundation-trained horse, will not need extra precautions. IF someone were forced to try this exercise and were dealing with any uncertainty in training levels or skills then some extra precautions would be called for. *(I recommend the use of a foot rope [see chapter fourteen] solely as a precaution. It should not be used unless absolutely necessary, which means to prevent a calamity.)* But I must repeat:

If you don't know what you're doing,
do the horse a favor and DON'T TRY THIS!

Hitching to the cart: Within the large open area available for driving, take the horse to the cart and allow him to see it and sniff it. Now, while someone else holds the horse's lead shank, move the cart around in front of the horse. Now circle the horse with the cart, or, if necessary, just walk the horse around the vehicle. With one person on the lead rope and one person on the cart shafts, carefully bring the vehicle forward with shafts raised to avoid contact with the horse until necessary. The person on the lead shank should take hold of the shaft tip on his side while the other person moves to the opposite side shaft. Now, while still holding the horse, lower the shafts and pass through the shaft loops. Before hitching take down the lines and pass back to the person at the vehicle. Do not pull on the lines unless required to stop the horse. That person holding the lines should fasten the hold-back straps and then the traces. The second person should remain at the head of the horse. The whip should be on the cart and handy to the driver. The driver now should get on the cart, careful not to lean on the lines, and the person at the head can remove the lead shank and stand available to assist. The driver will now think about baseball (try not to communicate any worry) and give the horse the command to go. As everything moves ahead, the shafts, and cart following, will be a slightly different sensation and it may cause a little anxiousness on the part of the horse. Go

a short distance, twenty to forty feet, and say WHOA. Expect a stop and make it so. Now go a little further the next time. Do this in increments while making a very gradual wide turn. Do not try sharp turns until the horse shows it is becoming accustomed to the shafts by its side.

Now call on your helper to assist. Have him or her stand near the head of the horse while you pull back on the lines and say a sharp BACK and release the lines. If the horse does not back up have your helper push, with finger tips, on the point of the horse's shoulder just below the collar at the same time that you say BACK. This will remind the horse of the desired movement. Once you have the horse successfully backed once, return to driving ahead. Do not be in a hurry for fancy maneuvers. Count it good to have a quiet willing horse move ahead, stop and stand for you. Make this a short lesson, fifteen minutes, and make sure you don't quit until things are right. Don't give the horse the idea that because it was upset you released it. A successful start and stop is plenty good for a cut-off point.

Now have your helper return to the horse's head and snap in the lead rope. Carefully get off the cart keeping the lines in hand. Undo both traces first and hang up. Keep lines in hand as you go to the opposite side of the cart from your header. While your header releases the hold-back strap on his side, keeping hold of a loose lead rope, you do likewise on your side. Now do up the lines on the hames. While your header holds the horse and guides the shafts from his side, you work the opposite side shaft as you carefully push it back until it is free from both sides. Try not to poke the horse with the shafts or drop them on the ground. Now hold the shafts up as your header leads the horse forward. Before you leave, turn the horse around and let it have a good look and sniff of the cart.

Follow the same procedure in subsequent hitchings and expand your driving routine slowly to include sharper turns and more backing. After you feel comfortable with your trainee's performance on the cart you may move on to other tools or procedures.

We don't have any broke horses to hook with.

The preferred scenario includes hitching for the first time with a well broke horse. If you do not have a well broke horse or access to one (consider borrowing one and while you at it borrow its owner as well!), and have two trainees to work together here is a recommendation of how to proceed.

Return to the round pen with each horse, individually, and repeat the driving training with an emphasis on the verbal WHOA performance. (See the section immediately preceeding this entitled *We only have one horse* and do all those round pen procedures!) Take the horses, one at a time, outside of the round pen for ground driving exercises. Now return to the round pen and rig the lines up to hitch the two trainees together for the first time. (See previous chapters and **The Work Horse Handbook** for setting up lines. If you don't know how to do this you shouldn't be going through these exercises with the trainees. Find some help.) Drive the pair around the round pen until they move well together. Be ready to be surprised how easily they take to working as a pair. You need to make a judgement at this point as to which of the two horses seems to be the less reliable. This horse will be the one wearing the ***buck back rope***. I suggest that with this team you hook to a wagon rather than a forecart for the first time.

Next, follow the hitching procedures outlined in the pictorial series of our **Preferred Scenario.** Or, if you prefer, Aden Freeman's system of hitching in chapter fourteen. Whatever you do use please always consider your safety and the safety and comfort of your horses first and foremost.

Preferred Scenario: First Time Hitching.

As my father alluded to in the foreword to this book, one of the most often used training systems of the "get-it-done" school was to hook the green horse up with a well-broke older horse and go to work. A bazillion horses were started this way, and many of them turned out excellent. And we employ this tactic often and with good rewards. But we also bring trainee horses with good foundation training completed and we have a couple of tricks and devices we use.

Opposite the first page of this chapter you may have noticed the drawing of the *buck back rope*. I came to use this device first as part of a multiple hitching program that allowed me to drive four-up, six-up or more with just two lines. (Please see **The Work Horse Handbook**). I just naturally evolved to using it for a training aid and precautionary insurance. It works so well that I'm sure it must have been used by others long before me. The *buck back rope*, if called into play, makes an anxious, or prone-to-run, horse pull the entire load with its nose. The side-bar, photos and drawings will, I am sure, explain its use.

I also occasionally use a brichen rope or strap. This keeps the team from spreading apart when I drive over the tongue for hitching. I use it only as a training device and caution should be taken not to become dependent on it.

And I often use a snubbing rope as an equalizer of sorts. This works to keep over anxious horses - broke or not - from lunging ahead of the other horses.

The last of the devices is used less often, it's a jockey stick. This keeps a horse or two horses from getting their heads together and fighting or rubbing.

All of the tools will make more sense after you go over the side-bars, pictures and upcoming text.

Preparatory note: Imagine you were hooked up to something you couldn't see and then asked to pull it around behind you. You might get a little anxious about whether or not it was animal, vegetable or corporate construction. It just might panic you a little. Same with horses. Real dividends are yours when you respect the horses desire and ability for understanding. Before hitching take your animals to the vehicle and let them check it out completely. Perhaps even roll it back and forth a little in front of them. It can make a huge difference.

The models for the first series of photos to follow are Polly and Anna, three year old Belgian sisters. We are hooking to our three-wheeled forecart (design diagram featured in **The Work Horse Handbook**) and our rubber-tired breaking wagon.

C. Once the fillies are standing where we want them we hook up the team lines. (They are not in any way hooked to the forecart yet.) Jess is straightening Polly's outside line. The lead ropes are hanging straight down and these alert, attentive, intelligent young horses are standing perfectly still as we EXPECT them to.

186

D. When the lines are properly hooked to the bits I pull them back to the forecart while Jess holds the team. Behind Jess is a forty acre hay field with no obstructions. And notice that the ground the forecart rests on is fairly level. This can be very important for first time hitching because you don't want the vehicle moving around while you're trying to get everything hooked up.

E. While I hold the lines slack, Jess hooks up the neckyoke.

G. Let us presume, for the sake of this demonstration that Polly, the right hand filly, is the better broke of these two. I hooked Anna's tugs first and I am hooking Polly's outside tug last. It is now that I would hook up the back end of the buck back rope. (See side-bar.)

F. While Jess stands in attendance at their heads I hook the traces calmly and quickly. Notice I hold the team lines in my hand. It is now that Jess would be hooking in the buck back rope to Anna's halter. (See side-bar.)

H. (right) Now I, with lines in hand, step up on the forecart while Jess ties the lead ropes to the outside hames of each filly.

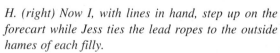

187

I. Jess is standing ahead of us to the right of the photo to see if I need any help with adjustments. I speak to the girls and they start out.

J. Jess gets on and we go for a little drive to line out the fillies.

Side-bar: Buck-Back Rope

Please see the illustration at the front of this chapter. Above: I am adjusting the buck back rope snap at the chain at the end of the double tree. The chain allows a range of adjustment. Jess is holding the lines and sitting on the wagon.

Above right: Here you can see the buck back rope at work. If Anna, on the left, wants to run or lunge ahead she must pull the entire load at the nose strap of her halter. The mouth, with this device, is left alone.

Right: You can see the white line of the buck back rope running to Anna's halter. In this manner she is mechanically discouraged from running or jumping ahead.

Side-Bar: Snubbing Rope (or Check Rope)

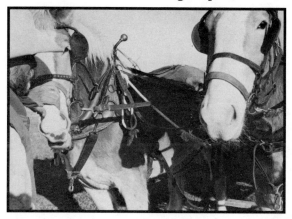

In this photo you can see that we have used a halter rope and snapped it into the bottom ring of Anna's halter and tied it back to the upper ring on Polly's inside hame. The rope needs to be adjusted so that it comes taught when Anna steps ahead of Polly. This works like the buck back rope but not quite as effectively. It is a good tool for getting a horse to slow down without having to yank or pull on the bit. It should not be used at the same time as the buck back rope. And if both horses are running it doesn't do much to slow down the outfit. The buck back rope at least forces the attached horse to pull the entire load.

After the first time hitch

A. This is what our low-rider breaking wagon looks like. It has an auto-steer front end and was home-made.

B. When we unhitch we leave the lines fastened and drive the team away from the tongue. Then we immediately return and drive the team over the tongue.

C. The second or third time we do this the team is willing to move into a pretty good hitching position. While they stand you should play with the harness.

D. Again I'm showing how is it that we teach the horses to move over against the tongue with pressure from the tug.

189

Side-bar; Brichen Rope and Strap

A long soft lead rope with a strong snap is fastened from one end of one horse's brichen to the other as shown. This rope holds the team together when crossing the tongue and backing into hitching position. A heavy adjustable leather strap with snaps on each end can be used on the inside, as shown, but is not as strong nor as effective as the rope.

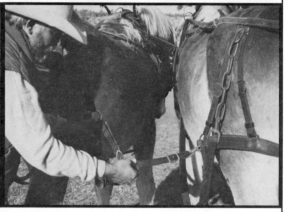

These two photos (above and above right) demonstrate the effectiveness of the buck back rope. Here Jess and I have hooked Queenie (his Percheron) to Barney (my Belgian). The rope shows up well as Queenie flies ahead and sideways in the right photo. It doesn't take very long for the excited horse to accept the fact that pulling with the nose is no fun.

It is important to have the rope properly adjusted so that there is relief when the trainee walks at the right pace and in the right place. That's why Jess is walking in the left picture. He's on the side where he can get to that rope and adjust it. If it's too tight there will be no relief for good behavior and the trainee may get balky. These two photos are by Sharon Ross.

Finishing Notes

A. *Here Jess is driving Lana (Belgian) with one of his Percheron mares, Lady. Jess's four black mares were put through the round pen acceptance training routine. They were then each driven, individually, with either Lana or Barney on this forecart or the breaking wagon. In this case the forecart is hitched to a pasture harrow.*

B. *In this picture you see Queenie and Barney again. You can see that she has calmed down and is working quite well. This might look easy but it does require a teamster who knows how much pressure to apply and what behavior to expect and allow from the trainee.*

C. *On the front cover of this book is a photo of this team on a mower. Red and Blue were put through the round pen acceptance training routine. After initial driving with Barney and Lana they were hooked together for extended drives on the breaking wagon. Jess took them for three separate one hour drives which included some hill sides where they learned to hold the load both at a stand and while being pushed down the grade. We were short a team to mow that summer so we decided to speed up the training on these two five year olds. The procedure we used worked extremely well and goes to the heart of the idea of preparing the horses to reduce surprises. (The two photos above and right are by Sharon Ross.)*

D. *Jess had a broke team on the mower cutting hay. I drove Red and Blue on the wagon and followed the mower. I got closer and closer until the mares could look down and see the cutter bar going back and forth. Then I passed the mower on the left and pulled in front of Jess so that Red and Blue could hear that mower coming up from behind them. After one pass around the field they seemed totally accepting. So we unhitched both teams and traded implements. I climbed on the mower and spoke to Red and Blue and Kristi took the photo on the front cover. What you see are the first steps these mares took the fourth time they were ever hitched and the first time hooked to a mower. Above is one week later. Testimony to the effectiveness of this training program.*

E. Here is a teamster's viewpoint of Jess's mares, Queenie and Molly, on one of their first time hitchings. Although they may look like they are perfectly broke, extra precautions are always taken to assure that NOTHING ever goes wrong.

F. Here are Jess's mares discing some plowed ground on Singing Horse Ranch. One problem area for less experienced teamsters arises when a team's level of training and trustworthiness is over-estimated. You must be vigilant in watching that everything is working properly and that your horses are comfortable.

G. Jess again with his mares on the mower. They look as though they've been doing this forever but it's their first time on this complex piece of machinery. The precision, repetition and progression of farm field work is excellent for providing a finish to the work horse's training.

H. Here Jess has hooked three of his mares abreast and to a disc. A month before this picture was taken these mares were going through the routines in the round pen. Having only weekends to work with them, they came along extremely well and in good speed.

Side-bar: Training for Work versus Training for Show

There are draft horse show people who believe that farm horses end up too slow to ever do well in the show ring. Ten years ago I visited with top hitch showman Harold McMain, at the Denver show, and he spoke of how he believed the best place to train hitch horses was on the farm manure spreader. Repetitious farm work does not make horses slow. Over work and rough handling of the mouth with poor feed and hoof care will result in ever slower horses. Proper overall handling and sensitvity on the lines always results in horses that are a delight to drive. It also results in horses better equipped to deal with the emotional stress of the show ring. While I am not a show person I do feel that the farm can be a real training ally for the show ring.

Hooking the trainee into the larger hitch.

In keeping with the idea that field work can be a real tonic and mental conditioner for the trainees, it may occur that you wish to add the green horse to a larger hitch. My personal preference of where to hook the newcomer is on the outside of that span closest to me. I want to able to reach that animal without having to get into the middle of the outfit should anything go wrong or get unhooked. These excellent photos illustrate one such potential problem. Imagine, if you will, that the offending horse were in the middle of this three abreast instead of on the outside. The resulting tangle would be that much more difficult and hazardous to repair.

*While on the subject of larger hitches (meaning more than two horses), it has been my experience that it is actually as easy to drive three or four or more horses as it is to drive two. And that these larger hitches can be an excellent place to "finish" a trainee. There seems to be a great potential for calming from the harnessed herd of trained horses that goes well beyond whatever is communicated by just one able partner. (For hitching diagrams and specifics see **The Work Horse Handbook**.)*

In these photos Jess and I are preparing to hook three abreast. We are using Barney (the sorrel) and Molly - and hooking Queenie in one of her earliest adventures. We intend to setup the lines and ground drive the three to a waiting disc where they will be hooked to the evener. We took advantage of this opportunity to setup a potential wreck and show you how we untangle it. This further illustrates how important your skill level is and why you should put a premium on able help.

A. The lines are all setup. Jess is behind with the lines in hand as I adjust the cross checks. Queenie is on the left of this picture. She has already started to move sideways, away from Molly.

B. You might pick up from this closeup that Molly is not happy about what she thinks is about to happen. C. & D. ....and below you see that Queenie is attempting to turn inside out. At this point Jess has no effective control over Queenie or the entire hitch.

193

E. Now you can see why Molly doesn't like this affair, she's being pulled from two directions. And Barney is convinced something is very wrong and would just like to leave.

F. Here's a closeup of what Queenie has done to herself. The lines are doubled back so that pulling on them does no good. At this point, if you were alone, you have a potential wreck on your hands. Something's got to give somewhere. Luckily we are dealing with two broke horses and all three have excellent "foundations" so they are paying attention to our whoas and calming words. And luckily I am in a position to do what I know I must do.

G. I go to the lines between Molly and Queenie, step Queenie ahead with her halter, and pull the check rein buckle back through the hame ring.

H. Next I hold Queenie in place while I step Molly ahead and nod to Jess.

I. I get out of the way and Jess drives them ahead knowing that the forward motion will prevent Queenie from repeating her maneuver. In a situation like this the knowledgeable teamster knows that any attempt to back up these three will result in the same tangle you just witnessed.

194

J. Here you see how Queenie is reacting to the affair. Before Jess gets into position at the disc evener, I make sure to unhook the evener from the disc (in such cases we use a quick attach or release hook with a keeper). When the horses are in position I go to Queenie and keep her still and in position. Jess, with lines kept in hand, hooks Queenie's evener first and then the other two. I then go to the back and hook the evener into the disc as Jess gets on the seat and prepares to go. When we unhook we reverse the routine, we unhook the evener from the disc and then unhook Queenie followed by the others.

K. A couple of weeks later; here are three of Jess's mares hitched to the three wheeled forecart and pulling the pasture harrow. That is Queenie in the middle for the first time. Notice her ears and head, she's certainly paying attention. Although she's come a long ways this is her first time having a horse on either side of her, so she's thinking about it a lot.

L. But as the work progressed that day it all became second nature and smooth.

Side-bar: The Jockey Stick

Sometimes you need to keep a horse from rubbing on or attacking the horse it is working with. A jockey stick serves this purpose. It is commonly snapped to either the outside bit ring of the offender (or preferably the halter ring) and back to the lower hame ring on the other horse.

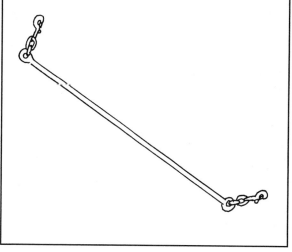

195

The Results

A. Here my son, Justin, prepares to drive two of Jess's mares into the wheel position...

B.... because Jess was hitching all four mares to his wagon. Three months before these mares first entered their training program. And they were lucky to have such an exceptional teamster as Jess to run them through their training.

C. & D. In these two photos you see how well this team (including Queenie and Molly) took to their first effort at logging. This is what you can expect from well-trained horses.

E. & F. And here Jess and I take turns with his mares on their first experience with the riding disc plow.

196

Chapter Thirteen

Correcting Problems

I will try to cover each problem area individually, as we might approach it, and then with other solutions. In most cases I believe you will find that the horse with a good foundation training will have none of these problems. I also believe that it is rare that a horse have just one problem, because the problem is often an indication of a larger set of circumstances which create an environment prone to problems. To explain I need to reiterate that:

1. What we see as a problem may be the horse's natural effort to protect itself and survive (i.e., runaway).

2. Or it may be a behavioral trait we inadvertently trained for (i.e., hard to catch).

3. Or it may be because we did not establish ourselves as the DOMINANT partner in a TRUSTING relationship. (i.e., biting and kicking)

4. And it may be because of natural deficiency in the individual horse (be it hereditary, disease or poor care) - (i.e., will not stand quietly).

5. But most likely it is a combination of one or more of these circumstances (i.e., balky).

I hope you can see by these variables that it is not enough to know WHAT the horse does wrong. You need to also know WHY before you can do an intelligent job of correcting the problem permanently.

If you start scratching a part of your body - because you are nervous about something extraneous - and a sore develops, putting on first aid cream and an anti-itch compound does not solve the problem of your nerves. Same is true with horses. Again this points to a return to the fundamentals of foundation training.

All that said, unfortunately we cannot be there to help you diagnose the horse's problem(s). If you are new to horses and find yourself confused, threatened, frightened, ineffective and/or troubled by traits your horse exhibits, you may have to find qualified help in the form of a skilled teamster who can work with you and the horse.

Over the last twenty years I have been frequently asked to diagnose the problem with this or that work horse. And I'm sorry to report that at least one third of the cases were problems created by the person owning and/or handling the horse. And another one third of the problems were solely with the people or in their heads (the horses had no behavior problems, they were fine!).

197

That left one third of the problems that fell into the catagory of "baggage". I say baggage because the horse brought it with him from wherever he got it. And, this is important, the people dealing with him seldom know the full and true nature of the baggage. For simple example; the horse might have had a bad experience with a previous home that resulted in a total unreasonable fear of steam whistles. Now whenever he hears a whistle or escaping steam he wants to get away, fast. But we don't know this. That's the worst kind of baggage because it creates a deep black hole in that horse's psyche. If we knew the root cause we could cleverly devise a way to safely return to the source of the terrible memory and allow the horse an opportunity to gain some courage in the face of it. But since we don't know we must do the best we can. (Again that often means returning to the round pen and teaching the horse that he has a protector [us] and teaching the horse a form of mental judo to deal with the boogey man [as the "roping out" does]).

Runaway Horses

We start with the big one first. At the risk of annoying you I must respectfully request that you read the entire text of this book before you attempt anything suggested here. I will not waste time talking about why horse's run away. It's in the remainder of this text. But it is enough for you to know that the horse is doing what comes natural to them when they feel frightened, threated, and sometimes when they are confused.

What We Do.

We gauge the level of the problem - safely. We hitch the offender to our breaking wagon, forecart or work sled with a good solid broke horse with the **buck back rope** properly rigged

(See chapter twelve). If the horse flies apart and throws a complete fit (he can't run away with our outfit) we know we will return to the round pen and start from ground zero with fundatmental training; all the while watching to determine if the problem is a lack of training, deep fears or mental/physical problems. If it is the latter we will correct the problem if we can, or dispose of the horse.

If when we do this initial trial-run we find that the horse's problem is not so dramatic, or doesn't immediately surface, we have some detective work on our hands. For the experienced teamster the "sleeper" is the more dangerous horse. By this I mean a horse that seems to go along pretty fine until, without warning, he or she goes berserk and must get away. Sometimes the source of the problem can be identified. Sometimes it cannot. If the horse cannot be driven, stopped and reasoned with you may have to get rid of it. Some of these horses have gone on to lead productive lives in the hands of capable teamsters who always watch them and protect themselves. You might not be able to do this.

You must allow yourself the possibility that the horse is beyond or outside of your ability to help it. Do not tie your future with work horses to the misery of an incurable horse.

If we have the benefit of dealing with a horse that is afraid of certain things - and we know what they are - we work, sometimes in the round pen and always in a safe place, to recreate the offense or fear and keep the horse in its presense until it becomes accustomed. You can imagine the myriad variables and perhaps forgive me for not trying to cover them here. I can only hope that what is presented in this book gives you a frame work to understand how to construct a successful correction.

The horse that runs away is refusing to accept your verbal command for WHOA, the line pressure on the bit, and its own knowledge (if properly trained) that escape is unneccessary and undesirable.

If you were not in control of the situation, the horse simply reverted to feral instincts and did what it had to. You were not in control if:

1. The harness was faulty.
2. You were absent from the scene.
3. The horse didn't trust you as an accepted dominant partner.
4. The horse wasn't properly trained.

Train the horse properly. Establish yourself as the caring boss. Make sure the harness and equipment is solid. And NEVER leave your horse unattended while hitched.

The horse that has run away several times has been subjected to a panic-flight resulting in a painful separation from the object of fright. In other words, the horse is actually trained, by unfortunate circumstance, to run harder and faster so as to get free of the source of fear. So you then have two problems to correct. One is the offending fear and the other is the horse's experience with running away.

If you have the opportunity there is one way to lessen or offset the character of the memory the horse retains of the runaway. Should you have a runaway experience you need to find a way to get that horse, or those horses, back out and working properly in harness IMMEDIATELY. I don't mean tomorrow or later in the day. I mean within the hour, preferably within the half hour. You've heard the old adage about getting back on the horse immediately when thrown off? That's because if you don't your last memory with riding horseback will be a frightening wreck and that memory has a way of swelling and etching into the psyche. The very same is true with horses. You need their last memory to be a good one, one that is firmly in your control.

If you must deal with the horse's fear some distance, after it has happened, the best approach is to return to the ***round pen/acceptance training*** and ***roping out***. There I reinforce the WHOAS in the round pen. By reinforce I mean repeat - repeat - repeat until it becomes monotanous. Then, and only then, change to a slightly more severe bit (the twisted double wire snaffle is my choice). And lastly I hook to a good, solid, broke horse (or horses) with the buck back rope and some long hours of hard work to do. Most of the time this will correct the problem but we must still be vigilant and keep a watchful eye on the offending horse. So you can see why it is important that his problem be handled by the skilled teamster.

The inexperienced teamster dealing with a chronic runaway horse is like someone welding around a gas station - sometimes you can do it successfully. If you are inexperienced, and find yourself in this boat, I recommend you get help either in the form of outside training for the horse or a replacement for the horse - or a ride-along teamster tutor.

Though I had several in the beginning, I have had only one runaway experience in the last fifteen years and that resulted because of complete equipment failure. First the neckyoke end of the tongue broke off, as we drove downhill, and within two minutes of trying to steer the horses clear of the swinging tongue one of the check lines came free of the conway buckle (I will NEVER use conway buckles at the check on team lines again!). Repairs were made and the horses were put back to work within one half hour after this problem.

But other runaways have occurred with my horses in my absense. During one summer I was deathly ill and had several people help with what little farming we managed. One of the men helping had apparently had some difficulty with the horses. As the story was unraveled I learned that this fellow had two of my broke horses on a harrow in plowed ground. During a break, while they were resting and he was smoking, something startled them and they jumped. Rather than reach for the lines he watched them run off across the field and stop. When I pressed him for some explanation he remarked "I ain't working here to get hurt. I could tell they were gonna run and it wasn't gonna do any good for me to be screaming or dragging along behind them!" Those horses would not have run if they had someone on the lines and offering at least a whoa, if not some reassurance. After that those horses never ran away with me and that man moved on to less demanding horizons.

As teamster it is your job and responsibility to look after your horse partners and that includes sticking with them in difficult situations. If you pitch the lines and step off whenever you feel the least bit threatened by their reactions or movements your cowardice will guarantee problem horses. Tractors were invented for people who are afraid of horses.

Other Approaches

The mechanics of *Foot Ropes* and *Running W's* are covered in chapter fourteen. They can be quite effective in teaching the horse the meaning of WHOA. (But mutual acceptance, choice and trust may be damaged or denied with the application.) They can be more or less abusive to the horse depending on the trainer. In the case of chronic runaways they can, if properly repeated, provide the intelligent horse the perception that they have a choice between behaving (stopping on command) or being dumped on their nose. You might succeed in removing running as an option. It should not, in my view, be seen as a replacement for good foundation training. Enough said.

There are measures which can be taken with **Bits and War Bridles**. In chapter four we have presented some drawings of designs of training bits formulated to provide tremendous punitive leverage to the horse's mouth as part of a program - 1st to train to stop on command - and 2nd to send a stronger message to the offending horse in a possible runaway situation. Again, it can be quite an effective approach in the hands of a skilled trainer, or a nightmare if abused.

The runaway horse may, from panic or cleverness, clamp its teeth down on the bit and thereby remove its effectiveness from the teamster. If you have ever seen a teamster see-saw the lines back and forth, they were either trying to free the bit from the clamp of the teeth or send a strong message to a misbehaving team.

The shank bit with curb chain, (there are many different styles), puts a vise-like pressure on the mouth and jaw simultaneously. More or less leverage is had by the relative position on the shank of the driving line. This style of bit is popular with show hitches and people concerned about being able to control the chronic runaway. A strong person pulling on the lines hitched to the bottom hole of a long shanked curb chain bit can break a horse's jaw. Repeated hard pulling may result in tenderness of the jaw bone and eventually a calcification.

Balky Horses

A few teamsters might agree with me that the balky horse is a worse offender than the runaway. With the balker you have a horse that has decided it will not go. It has checked out the situation and decided - *Nope, I'm better off if I stay right here.*

There is one infrequent but important exception; the horse that is in an advanced state of panic or shock and incapable of movement. And such a condition can be caused by more than the possible trauma of being hitched.

*In 1976, I was working four abreast on a disc for a week and the following Monday morning one of my regular and dependable workhorses, Dick, refused to move after hitching. I went to him to scope out the problem and found him glassey eyed and shaking. As I stood stroking his sweating neck he crumpled and fell to the ground. I later found he had **Azoturia** or **Monday Morning Sickness** (see **Work Horse Handbook**) from an improper feeding program. He survived and I learned a big lesson.*

What We Do

A true Balky horse is one which has "decided" not to go. And "deciding" means, to a more or less degree, it has denied your dominance in the relationship. If, through foundation training and mutual acceptance, you have firmly established yourself it is much less likely such will ever occur. However, the well trained intelligent horse, that has come to be convinced it is being abused, may refuse to start. For example the overworked horse, the hungry horse, the sore-footed horse may decide "enough is enough." I applaud them. The good teamster never allows such abuse to occur. And the good teamster knows how to read the signs to differentiate a legitimate health or threat related circumstance which mitigates the horse's refusal. If you misread the reason for the balk you may, by your actions, be creating a chronic balker.

If the horse's first complete refusal to proceed is met by whipping and yelling, a transition often occurs. The horse continues its original passive refusal to proceed but it also may become angry and defensive. If this horse makes an effort to bite or kick, and the whipping lets up or quits, a clear message is sent that the person's dominance is being forfeited. The horse gets the idea that it has won its argument. I am not suggesting that this is reason enough to accelerate whipping. Rather I am saying that the whipping, as soon as it becomes an emotional extension of the teamster, is a lost cause. In a particular situation there are tricks, under *Other Approaches*, that may be successfully used to temporarily reverse the situation.

But before I give you those tricks I need to say that at the core of the mutual acceptance round pen training is the gradual establishment of your acceptable dominance, reinforced by the imprinting that occurs through repetition. All that is to say, we can return to the foundation training and establish or re-establish ourselves as the boss and a friend. As the boss of the teamster-horse partnership our leadership would not be disputed, so long as we respected the horse's intelligence and made an effort to understand the reason. Here's an example from my experience:

Cali and Lana are not balky horses, they are one of my truest teams. Two years ago I purchased a brand new work harness for them and put it on to go do some field work. As I was getting ready to go out and hitch, two draft horse people showed up at the ranch. They wanted to watch me work, so after a few minutes conversation I proudly took my good mares in their brand new harness out to the forecart for hitching. I noticed that Cali seemed antsy but I ignored her. All hooked up, I spoke to the team and they leaned forward and Cali immediately flew back. She had never done this before and I confess to some embarrassment as these two guys were smirking. I then made a mistake in judgement, I hollered at the team and struck Cali with the end of the line - they moved ahead maybe five feet before stopping and refusing to go. The one man said ,"They haven't worked much, have they?" and the other followed suit with, "I wouldn't let them get away with that if I were you." I was mad, but now my anger had shifted from my good team to these visiting know-it-all clowns. I noticed that Cali was dancing in place and had her ears flat back. I went to her side and immediately noticed a thin trickle of blood coming from under the tug about six inches back from the collar. Lifting the tug at this point I could immediately see a small hole in her hide. I ran my hand under the trace and found that this new harness had a nail sticking through the thick portion of the tug about 1/4 inch. I took my neckerchief out and put it between the tug and Cali's shoulder, stroked and apologized to the mare, unhitched the team and got some tools to repair that problem. My two visitors leaned on the hood of their truck and mumbled to one another as they watched. Harness repaired I hitched back up to the forecart, spoke to my team and they started fine so we went to the field to work. The visitors left to tell stories about my incompetence with horses. Thinking back over the situation I'm pretty sure I would have gone to Cali immediately, to see if she had a detectable problem, had I been alone. But I aggravated the problem by letting my foolish pride and the visitors affect me. But imagine what might have happened had I persisted with beating and yelling at the mare to try to get her to go? Cali is not a balky horse. She had a totally legitimate excuse for not wanting to move ahead into that nail.

Other Approaches

An ingenious trick to cure the balky horse was presented in the book **Horse Sense** by J.C. Curryer (circa 1900). A rope is tied firmly into the doubled-back end of the offending horse's tail so that there are two differing lengths of rope hanging from the knot (see drawings). The short length is true so that if you pull on it you pull on the horse's tail. The longer length is a slip knot. If you pull on this the knot comes free of the horse's tail. Tie the short end of the rope to the end of the doubletree, and have the long end near you on the wagon or implement. Tap the other horse (the good one) to go and as he steps ahead he will pull sharply back on the offending horse's tail by way of the evener. The balker will move ahead thinking he will get rid of the pressure on his tail. Stop and start again. Each time watching to see if the balker is any more willing to start on his own. If he is, as they are moving ahead pull on the long rope and thereby release the tail knot. After a little driving stop your horses and start again. If the horse should balk, retie the knot and have him start the load with his tail again. This time drive to where there is a nearby downhill grade and and untie the rope as the horses are moving down. Stop your team on the grade and restart them. The grade itself will apply some forward pressure on the brichen or collar. Repeat this exercise until the balker is cured.

Another similar trick is to use a long girth rope (see next problem ***Pulling Back***) and have someone standing well ahead, available to pull on the rope as you give the command to go. This does not work as well as the tail rope because you do have to stop and take the rope off in order to proceed to work.

THE BALKY HORSE HITCHED
FOR THE START

Will Not Pull

You can have a horse that will start a light load willingly but refuse to pull a load of any weight. This is specialized and different from what we described in balking. And this may be easier to cure.

What We Do

With this circumstance the first thing that comes to mind is the fit of the collar. If the collar is either too big or too small it can cause the horse to refuse, for self-preservation and general reasons of discomfort, to pull. Make sure the collar fits properly.

The second thing that comes to mind is the condition of the shoulder. Check to see if there are any swollen areas or hot spots anywhere that the collar makes contact. Usually a sore shoulder is the result of an ill-fitted collar. However there are times when putting horses to too much work without gradual conditioning can result in sores.

The third thing to look at is experience. I once purchased a well broke pair of geldings who had always worked on the lead of an eight horse hitch. They had never been asked to pull something heavy. When I set to work with them they would hesitate and they would wander and wallow and bump into one another. it took a week and a half of regular field work before they learned to handle it. After that they seemed to actually relish the challenge of a difficult pull.

The best way to develop willing pullers is to build them up gradually. I like to pick field stones with a team for this purpose. As you load the stone boat or wagon the load gets gradually heavier. You unload and start all over again. I also like to take a hesitant puller out with good horses on the plow. If possible I use more horses than I need so that the job is comfortable for all.

Other Approaches

I have heard that some people use electric cattle prods to get their horses to pull. DO NOT do this! It will violate any trust you have built up with the horses.

Pulling Back

The horse that pulls back when tied up is a danger to itself and you. This habit is usually developed or inadvertently trained for through circumstance. A young frightened horse, tied up in a strange environment will fly back and try to escape as a natural act of self-preservation. If the rope or snap or anything involved should break and free the horse, even if only momentarily, the horse has learned that flying back or pulling back will result in release.

What We Do

If the horse has a proper foundation training and is tied in familiar and comfortable surroundings for its first experiences, and NEVER ALLOWED TO BREAK FREE, this problem will not develop.

Whenever we tie up a stallion in close proximity to other horses we double tie. There is the customary rope snapped into the halter, and there is a secured chain passing through the halter and around the stallion's throat.

Other Approaches

Use a strong halter, a large strong harness hardware ring, and a twelve foot long 3/8" to 1/2" in diameter. Braid in a bull snap to one end and a loop in the other. Pass the rope around the horse's girth and through the loop, so it slips free, and up between the front legs through the halter then through the an-chored ring and back to the halter (see diagram). IMPORTANT: If anything breaks when the horse

pulls back you will have aggravated the situation and made the horse worse. Make sure everything is solid. Now, with the horse tied in this manner either make the horse pull back or stay in attendance until it does. When the horse pulls back he will pinch himself and jump forward. It may take two or three such experiences to effect a cure. But you must make sure he is cured before you tie him in the old way. This could mean shaking a blanket or some other object to see if he will fly back after his initial three tests.

Kickers

The horse that kicks is either in a last resort defensive mode or, much worse, it has learned to use its feet as a weapon in order to get its own way. In either case the well-trained horse DOES NOT KICK. If it does it is because the person in charge has allowed it.

What We Do

The kicker is the horse who has denied the teamster his or her authority in the relationship. We recommend a return to the basics. For a thorough description of our procedure please see chapters nine through eleven and look to ***Roping Out*** and the subsequent information on training the horse to allow its feet to be handled.

Other Approaches

Through the years there have been various mechanical systems devised that either restrict the kicker or provide that it punish itself when kicking. One such setup is diagramed here. These can be dangerous and wholly ineffective in the hands of a novice.

Biters

Horses are either allowed to bite or trained to bite. In the beginning it may start as nothing more than a foals playfully nibbling on clothing or the attempted bite of a protective nursing mare. Don't allow young horses to nibble on you. A quick slap to the neck will communicate your point. And should an occassion arise when a mature horse feels compelled by natural instinct to bare its teeth towards you make sure you communicate your displeasure immediately. It may be enough to raise your voice. Beatings are not called for.

What We Do

Again we return to the acceptance training and roping out for tremendous results. But keeping in mind that to be truly effective it must be done by a caring knowledgeable person who WILL NOT BACK DOWN and who will always insist on being in charge. A great deal of the effectiveness of these measures is tied back to the attitude and approach of the person.

Over twenty years ago my old friend Ray Drongesen went to look at a stallion that was for sale. The man who had him was afraid of him and told Ray not to go into the pen without a whip or something. Ray ignored the man and went into the pen and the Percheron stallion charged. Ray raised his hand and said in a firm voice "that's enough of that!" The stallion stopped and allowed Ray his inspection. Ray bought that horse and worked him 3 or 4 days a week for several years and bred many mares. The stallion was attentive, gentle and eager. But I would hazard a guess that if the previous owner had ever tried to cross his space he would have reverted to past behavior. It was Ray's manner, as much as anything he actually did, that communicated to this horse.

Will Not Lead

Many a broke work horse is a dunderhead or pain in the fannie to lead. It shouldn't be this way and it does point to something lacking in the foundation of this horse.

What We Do

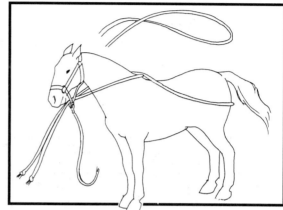

It's beginning to sound like a broken record but I must recommend you return to the training outlined in chapters nine through eleven. If you need some immediate quick help look to the information on Butt Ropes in chapters eight and nine. If you have to resort to a tug of war you are a long ways from where you should be. The horse needs to want to follow you and your direction. The lead rope should be a secondary means of control.

And the person who allows their horses to drag them around or take the lead away is not doing themselves any favors either. You need to establish yourself as the dominate member of the team.

Mean to Teammate

Horses, in this respect, are like people. Some of them get along famously and others just don't like each other. Two horses that have worked a lifetime together, always working on the same side, may not take lightly to being mixed up with other horses - whether in replacement or as larger hitches. But so what. Aren't you in charge, and don't you need to get the work done?

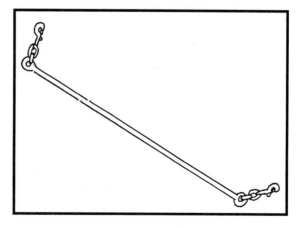

When training horses I recommend that you mix them up, work them occasionally on opposite sides - in the middle of three or four abreast - on the wheel or in the lead. Horses are creatures of habit. If you allow them to they will stake a claim. In a severe situation you can use a jockey stick to keep two horse's heads apart (recommended in certain setups involving stallions). But I prefer to have horses that will listen to me. If things aren't right I let them know through my voice and perhaps a quick jerk on the offending horse's line, punctuated by a "what are you doing?" couched in the tones of a tired and cranky daddy.

I once purchased a team of mares and was told by the seller that I had to keep them apart or they'd kick each other. These mares didn't like each other much. When I took them home I put them together, fed them together, made them share everything. In the beginning the one mare staked a claim and ran off the other, but in time they grew to be a real team. So often we don't realize that our efforts to prevent something from happening actually makes it happen.

Shies

When a horse jumps at every little thing, seemingly afraid of its own shadow, it can be a real nuisane.

What We Do.

The foundation training routine, and especially the roping out procedure, addresses this problem very well. Remember that with this amazing beast you can successfully build its courage. And also that you have an oportunity to be a trusted friend and ally, someone who will help the horse handle the heebee jeebees.

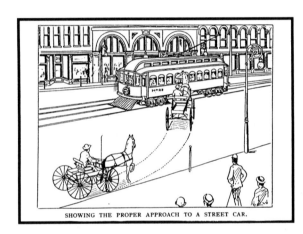

SHOWING THE PROPER APPROACH TO A STREET CAR.

We should mention however, that there can be health reasons why a horse shies. I had a gelding once that reacted in a peculiar manner. I had difficulties getting him properly trained. There did seem to be a pattern to his jumpiness but I couldn't figure it out until a veterinarian diagnosed him as three quarters blind in one eye. So I now conjecture that there was a range of his vision that didn't work and every so often he was surprised to find something come into view. If you have a severe problem with a shieing horse that no level of courage building seems to help, have a vet check its eyes.

On the other side, I like a horse that notices things. My friend Jess talks about the horse that "rattles". He likes a rattling horse. By rattle he's referring to the curious noise a worried horse makes which sounds like a combination snort and lip snapping. The horse that notices things and is allowed space and trust to figure them out is much less likely to full-out spook than the dopey horse that is surprised at the last minute by some oddity.

Other Approaches

In the next chapter you will see some of the mechanics of old-time training systems that involved complete subjection (or submission). The horse that shied and/or ran away would be thrown and held down while umbrellas, horns, bells and plastic were introduced. The theory was that when the horse was let up he would be unafraid of these things. As you might well imagine, there was a lot of subtlety and skill required to make such an approach less than a dangerous disaster.

Hard to Harness
Hard to Catch and Halter
Will Not Stand Quietly
Hard To Hitch

I have lumped all these together because they are, in my view, all related. I don't mean, necessarily, that a horse will have all these problems but that the prevention and cure is the same, *foundation training*.

What We Do.

Look to chapter four to see how a well-trained horse should react to harnessing.

Look to the sessions with Ted in chapter ten and Juniper in chapter eleven to see that there is no "catching" involved and haltering can be fully acceptable to the horse.

And look to chapter twelve to see how a horse should behave when you need them to hitch and stand quietly. All of this is acheived in the foundation training. If you have any of these problems I recommend you go back to square one and train for the sort of horse you want.

Other Approaches.

Hard to harness was usually handled in the old days the same as a horse that shies. With the special additional trick of tying up one leg to make the horse stand still while harnessing.

The other three problems were all seen to be the result of insufficient work. It was argued that if you worked a horse long enough and hard enough they would be easy to hitch, willing to stand and be waiting at the gate for the halter. I believe that it was less a result of the long hours of work than of the repeated handling required to get the work done. And I also believe that the results of the repeated handling can be duplicated in a fraction of the time with clever foundation training. The horse that's fed in the barn will wait at the gate for haltering.

Working Nursing Mares

You might reasonably wonder why I include this under correcting problems. Those of you who work mares and want to raise foals will find there will likely come a time when you have to figure out some way to be able to work those nursing mares without a lot of trouble. And boy can they give you trouble, especially if they are good mothers with all maternal instincts in place. But there is at least one way to have a relatively quiet and hassle free working separation. Gary Eagle was the first one to point me in the direction of daycare centers for foals.

You are one step ahead of the process if you have imprinted the foal. And if you have more than one foal it helps some.

What We Do

For the sake of simplicity I'll describe a situation involving a team of nursing mares. If we expect to work them, we feed the mares tied in a double tie stall of the same configuration as diagramed in chapter three. Adjoining that stall is another, same design. Only with this second stall we have put a gate across the front to convert it to a box stall. We call this our "day care center". Then at least one day before we are going to separate the mares from the foals, we have the team securely tied in their stall and eating. We halter the foals and lead them in the barn alley and perhaps even outside. If the mares and foals talk to one another we ignore it. After fifteen minutes we leave the halters on the foals and release them. They will return to their anxious mothers and often go to nursing. One hour later we take those two foals into the adjoining box stall where the manger is full of hay and the grain boxes have a little calf manna and rolled ration (one half pound in each). We play with the foals a little and then take their halters off and leave them shut in the stall. With the half partition divider the tied mares can see their babies. We then work on cleaning the barn and oiling harness or machinery for an hour, careful to be nearby and available if something should happen to cause potential harm to mares or foals (care must be taken that the foals don't lay down and put legs under the gate). If the mares scream and/or the foals scream we ignore it. At the end of that hour we open the day care center gate and turn the foals loose. They run to their mothers and ram their noses into the udders to drink.

If we have the luxury of time we will repeat this routine once again, maybe even that same day. The mares learn that the foals are just a short distance away and okay. The foals seems to enjoy going into the "day care center" where the free-choice feed is waiting. The next day we put the foals into the day care center and harness the mares. Then we take the team out to do some job that might take about an hour. We are careful, for this first time, not to get the mares too hot as this can have an affect on the character of their milk and give foals the scours if they are allowed to drink it immediately. When we return to the barn with the mares we turn

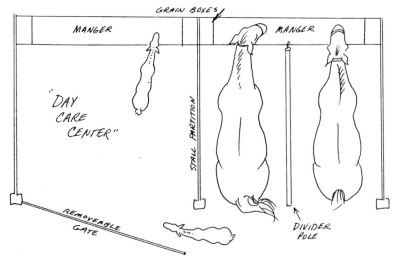

the foals loose. They run to the mares and ram their noses into the udders. The mares immdiately learn that the foals are okay and the ramming seems to send another message.

Healthy foals pester their mothers, just as healthy infants can drive their human mothers nuts. Most human mothers would welcome an opportunity to go shopping or visiting or to work in the garden, if they knew their children were being properly and safely cared for. Same with horses. Some of you are shaking your heads and you think this is another piece of nonsense. Our experience has shown us that the mares who are separated from their foals and taken to the field for work most definitely enjoy the break. And the foals with a familiar surroundings, food, and another foal or two to play with, get right into the habit.

Many a visitor has been surprised to see us open the day care center gate and say *okay you guys its time to go to work, get in here.* And surprised to see the foals walk right in. And surprised to watch us drive the mares away to the field with nary a nicker to be heard.

This whole day care center business is excellent training for the foals. It is an easy way to work towards building their courage and self-reliance early on.

Other Approaches

Yes, you can take your foals along when you drive the mares. Obviously there should be intelligent concern for the age and health of the foal relative to the amount of time you'll be driving and the general surface conditions (i.e., plowed ground, paved road, mud, etc.). For the longest time, whenever I tied a foal to the mare to walk along while I worked, I tied the lead rope to the second hame ring of mama's harness. My friend Jess Ross taught me a safer and more intelligent place to tie. He ties the foal to the belly band billet at the tug and long enough so the foal can nurse whenever the mare has stopped. This way the foal cannot get around in front of the mare and get tangled in the end of the neckyoke.

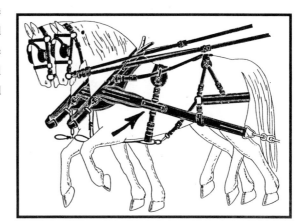

Robert Clark (lead wagon) and L. R. Miller (second wagon) pull Grund hill on the Flathead Indian Reservation in Northwestern Montana.

Chapter Fourteen

Important Training System Variations and Alternatives

In keeping with our promise that this book would contain different ideas on the subject of training we offer this important chapter. It begins with a discussion about turn of the century training techniques and devices including **running W's** *and* **foot ropes.** *It then moves into the specific approaches of some named and un-named SUCCESSFUL teamster- trainers working today. A highlight of this chapter, and even the book, is a photo study of the training technique employed by my good friend and legendary Canadian teamster Aden Freeman.*

Please do not get the idea that this chapter contains ideas which are opposite to mine, and thereby somehow judged as inferior. This is most certainly not true. I personally know of horses, trained employing many of the ideas presented in this chapter, which I would be proud to own and which would no doubt whup me in a plowing match. Like I keep saying, I believe there is no ONLY way.

Old Ways

Back in the Fall and Winter of 1986 we reprinted a large part of an old book entitled **HORSE SENSE,** by J.C. Curryer, in the **Small Farmer's Journal.** The book was loaned to us by good friend and Iowa horsefarmer, Judson Schrick. The book was originally published in 1900. I learned a great deal from that text and found some material to disagree with. But I was originally drawn to it because it offered some unique differences from the run-of-the-mill *SUBJECTION / SUBMISSION* training techniques which predominated from 1850 to 1950. While it differed from what came before and after, it also employed many of the same devices. I choose not to employ most of the devices but I embrace many of his precepts. I'd like to begin this chapter by offering some of those precepts and then a synopsis of the procedure and devices. What follows immediately are direct quotes from Dr. J. C. Curryer M.D. and horse trainer (I might add horse champion and psychologist).

There is certainly one point decidedly in favor of the horse in respect to his education, and that is, that whatever he learns and understands he never forgets; and this cannot be truthfully said of all men. Horses, like people, have strong likes and dislikes, and where one educator succeeds, another will fail. It is all in the horse and man thoroughly understanding, or not understanding each other, and by mutual consent being friends or enemies.

The earlier we begin the education of our horses the more valuable servants they make, and the more money they will bring in the market. The horse appreciates kind, intelligent treatment as well as man, and when the horse and his tutor fully understand each other, it is astonishing how rapidly the horse acquires his education.

Far too many of the horse's captors, owners and drivers have considered him only a "brute" to be yanked, kicked, pounded and neglected to man's passion, indifference and sometimes pleasure.

Many books on training have been printed, many horse trainers have traveled the country over, and many devices have been used to take advantage of the horse's muscular strength, with the sole idea of subduing, conquering, overpowering and punishment. But the true principles and natural laws that govern the horse's actions for easy and natural compliance with the wishes of man have been ignored, unknown or misunderstood. And in too many instances the very means that were intended to aid in the management of the horse, have proved added tortures to him, from a non-compliance of the natural laws governing the actions of the horse. Nearly all the bad actions of our horses are the results of misplaced confidence, confusion and a misunderstanding of his nature, abuse from his handler or trying to force him to do what he does not understand. We should always work according to the laws governing the horse's actions and above all, be sure the horse fully understands what we want him to do, and at the same time treat him with the utmost kindness, then he will appreciate what we do for him and in turn, do for us all he is capable of without complaint.

We must first understand the underlying principles or natural laws governing the actions of our animals. If the horse is secure at one end of the body only he is sure to go in the opposite direction for relief. Fasten him at the front end of the body and he naturally goes backwards to free himself. If fastened at the rear end only, he as naturally goes forward to get away from the object of attack. These natural laws are instinctively and constantly complied with in the action of our horses, and whatever we have to do with them must be in accordance with these laws, if we desire safe, reliable and enduring animals.

We are all aware that many will say that the bit is the only means of controlling and directing our horses, and "with the whip in one hand and the lines in the other, we can force him to do our bidding." Yes, this can be done only to a limited degree, but to have the best service of your horse he should understand what is wanted of him and then he will gladly

214

and willingly comply. But if we rely only on the lines and whip then we will have horses that are not to be trusted.

Punishment bits are intended to overcome the mischief already done by some bungling, unthinking, unfeeling and careless handler; but we are sorry to say that, as a rule, they result in making a bad matter worse.

With the punishment by the whip at the rear end of the animal, and a harsh and mutilating bit at the front end, the horse is between two fires; and if he does not balk, rear, plunge, and run away, it is a wonder.

Curryer's training routine begins with a belief in the use of sugar and sweet treats to gain the favor of the young horses. Then he believes in exercising the foals, up to four at a time, by tieing them into a custom affair that is basically a cart with outriggers (see drawing) with an old broke horse in the shafts. He then drives this outfit through all manner of hazards to acquaint the young horses with all that might startle them later in life.

The old horse teaching the weanling colts.

Driving on the road.

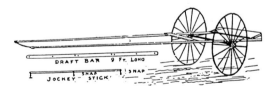

Combination cart.

215

Though Curryer makes an eloquent case for a gentle approach to training he does, I believe, contradict many of his precepts with his insistance that the mature horse's training begins with what he calls a *safety bridle* (what is generally referred to in these days as a *war bridle*.)

The basic principle of a war bridle (I no longer use one) is that you inflict a sharp pain and offer relief the instant the horse complies or becomes passive. Curryer's description reads as thus:

The main principle of handling the horse through the medium of the mouth is to have the punishment happen at a distance from you and if he does not come to you for relief, you should go to him and relieve him of any undue pressure that has been brought to bear on his mouth; assuring him that when near you he can get relief, which he will learn in one or two minutes and be willing to follow you wherever you may go. It is always better to make your impression on his mouth when he is at an angle, instead of in front of him. This will induce him to turn on his hind feet and advance towards you, when you should relieve him every time, if he is in the least trouble.

Here are drawings from his books of the safety bridle and the so called "Yankee bridle."

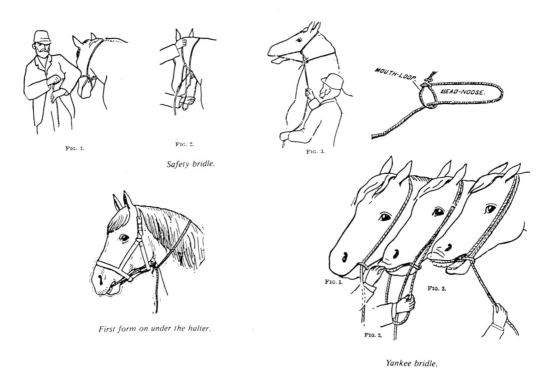

FIG. 1. FIG. 2. FIG. 3.

Safety bridle.

First form on under the halter.

FIG. 1. FIG. 3.

FIG. 2.

Yankee bridle.

216

Curryer believes in training horses from their first day of life but he recognizes that many older horses need training. His approach to these includes a classic, severe approach to subjection and submission. He does not see it as severe. Here are his words.

There is probably nothing we ever do to the horse that is quite so assuring him of our superior power, like that of laying him down and putting him in a perfectly helpless condition and at the same time, treating him with the greatest kindness.

We offer here the drawings, from Curryer's book, of his system for laying down a horse.

THE HORSE ALREADY TO BE LAID DOWN

218

THE HORSE IN A COMFORTABLE POSITION

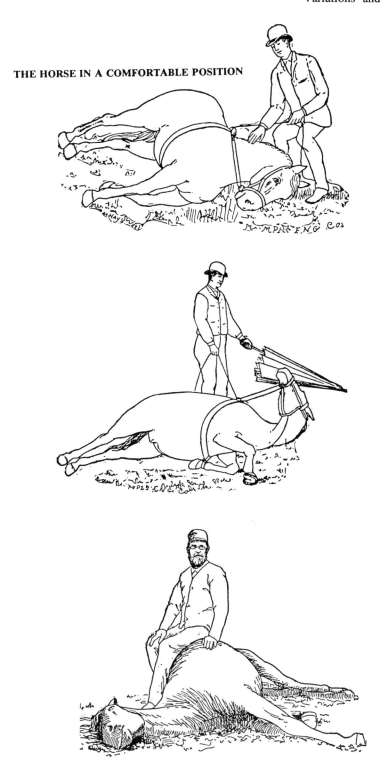

Curryer finishes his approach with the advice that the laying down of the horse may not work fully for a truly hard case. He goes on to describe what we commonly refer to now as a **Running W** and how he "handles the horses legs." Those drawings are included here.

For a look at Curryer's approach to balkers and kickers see chapter thirteen, Correcting Problems, of this book.

THE WOULD-BE RUNAWAY SECURED

**CONVINCING THE HORSE OF HIS UTTER
HELPLESSNESS**

Running W's and Foot Ropes

One of the most common systems of training work and general driving horses employs the Running W as cornerstone.

The Running W is a rigging outfit, homemade or otherwise, which seems to allow a person to pull both front legs out from under a large horse while it is moving. In truth the rigging allows that a person of moderate bulk and strength can pull the horse's front feet up to the belly when they are on the back side of any stride. (If the front legs are fully extended foreward this rigging does not give anyone enough leverage to pull the legs back under the belly and up.) The diagrams on the two preceeding pages do well to show what occurs. The diagram on this page better illustrates the workings of the rigging. It's called a W because of the shape made by the rope "running" from side to pastern to belly to pastern to side.

A VIEW FROM THE MIDSECTION UNDER-BELLY OF THE HORSE

RUNNING W

Many exceptional teamsters train their horses by getting them into harness as quickly and simply and they can; and rigging the harness with a full running W. And then, usually with a second person in attendance on the "trip rope," they drive them, with another horse, prepared to drop them when they do not stop. (The usual rule is say WHOA twice and on the third WHOA, if he is still moving, drop him.) If the running W is employed while a horse is walking, the result is a stumbling hop on knees until he finally stops. If the rigging is employed when a horse is running it results in a complete and sudden fall to the knees, and sometimes a rolling to one side. People I know who use this device to train their horses to stop claim they have never done permanent damage to any horse. Some people use it only in grass fields, others use it while on the pavement or gravel. I do know of horses which suffered severe physical harm from being dropped, at a dead run, on pavement. The owner who told me this added that the horse had to learn.

I did use a running W once and did not like the results. I have not used it since. My friend, Jess Ross, has never used a running W. My mentor Ray Drongeson did not use a running W. But I do know teamsters, that I have a great deal of respect and admiration for, who regularly use it.

We have to remind ourselves that this Running W business is either a tool or an approach. As a tool it is neither good nor bad because it can be used in such different ways. As an approach, a belief in the use of the Running W may be dangerous because it might blind the trainer to other ways which can give better, more lasting, results.

As a tool I can perhaps give a pretty good word picture of how various it may be. Imagine that you have a trained horse which has been "allowed" to runaway several times. As I suggested earlier you may have "Trained" that horse to run. The horse DOES know what WHOA means, he has just decided to over-rule that command; whether the root cause is panic or orneriness doesn't matter - only that he isn't accepting the command. The running W could be put on this horse and used in the safest possible environment to remind him of your authority. Instead of using it to drop the horse that is running, you can use it while he is walking and only when he refuses to stop immediately on command. In this way you are only taking away his dominance, you aren't hurting him. If, instead, you simply use the device to drop a horse, because it's running and won't stop on your command, ask yourself what you're training for? The horse will figure out that whenever you are driving, and he runs, you WILL drop him on his nose and he won't be sure why. It won't take very many experiences with this routine and the horse will become unruly. He will associate you, the harness, hitching and pulling something all with the inevitability of him being dumped on his nose. Any mutual acceptance and trust is out the window.

So, the challenge is with you to decide if you will use it, how you will use it, and how to use it and maintain a trusting relationship with your horses. It can be done but it requires some special skills and strong empathy for the horse. I hope, through the bulk of the text that has preceeded this, that I've succeeded in offering you a strong assortment of alternatives.

Foot ropes differ dramatically from the running W if only in the reduced leverage, and therefore their applicability. A foot rope is usually understood to be a solitary rope that passes through an anchor point on the side of the horse and on down to the pastern. (Please see the diagram on this page). They can be used to send a strong message to the uncooperative walking trainee that WHOA means stop. But please understand that the foot rope does not offer enough leverage and effectiveness to control or stop a runaway horse.

Foot ropes and foot straps are not the same. Foot ropes can be immediately released and from behind the horse. Foot straps hold a leg fixed and are usually employed to force a horse to stand still sometimes for sacking out, sometimes for saddling, sometimes for vet or farrier care.

Breaking Rig: Center Pivot

About ten years ago I had occasion to visit Percival Griffin in Maine and he showed me his ingenious horse training system based on a special device. I have since seen similar outfits around the country and found this 100 year old engraving of the same rig in our archives.

The principle is that the horse is harnessed and hitched between the wheels. The teamster sits and gives the command to go and touches the horse with the whip. The horse goes and perhaps even takes off at a run. But it doesn't matter because the solidly built breaking rig just keeps the horse going around in a circle. When the horse slows to stop the teamster tries to coincide the stop with a WHOA command. Then the horse is started again and the routine is repeated. After some success with the procedure the horse is taken off. The next day the horse is hitched to go in the opposite direction. This procedure is repeated as often as it takes until the horse stops and goes on command.

Bob Oaster's System

A good friend of mine from Michigan, with a long history working farm horses, described for me a system which employed a special foot rope apparatus. The apparatus is not so important. But Bob Oaster's technique is. He would gentle his horses and then rig a foot rope that would allow him to pull a foot or two up from a distance. He would then take the trainee into a barn alley or corral space and place only the foot ropes on the horse, no halters or harness or bridles. He would then have them walk away and give a verbal WHOA command while simultaneously pulling on the rope and making the horse come to a gentle stop. He would repeat this program until the horse would stop at the softest whoa. Only then did he proceed to accustom the horse to harnessing and hitching,

Aden Freeman's Training System

Aden Freeman farms in Ontario, Canada, between Ottawa and the St. Lawrence River. I became acquainted with Aden, and his family, when doing Workhorse Workshops in that part of the world. Aden is one of a group of truly fine teamsters who helped me and worked to keep me honest. Aden is an artist with a work horse and with the walking plow. He is also a very good farmer. Ruth and Rita Freeman, Aden's daughter and wife, took a set of photographs a couple of winters back of the training of two Belgian fillies and we are fortunate in being able to offer them here as an important alternative system. I trust the captions will tell the whole story.

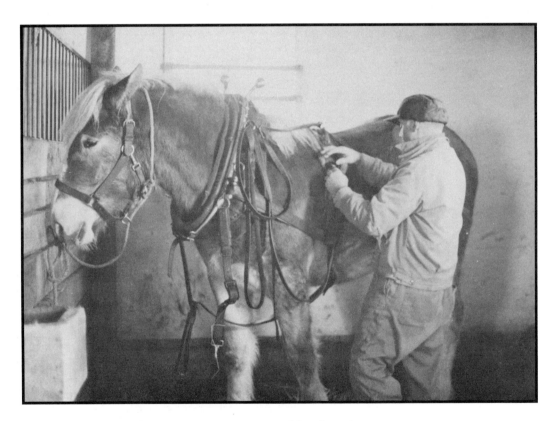

A. This is Mabel, at the time of this photo she was one and a half years old. Aden has fooled with this filly, in the barn, for a week. This the first time she was harnessed. He has secured her, in the box stall, with a neck rope in case she was frightened by the harnessing. Before harnessing, Aden introduced the bit and let her eat her hay with the bit in the mouth.

B. This is the second method of harnessing. Mabel is cross-tied in the barn. this method has advantages because the mare can't chew or rub on the harness. And because the filly can't crowd the person harnessing. Mabel was harnessed and left cross tied in the barn six times before being hitched. At the end of the week she was completely happy with the harness.

C. In this picture you see Don, a 10 year old Percheron cross gelding, being readied to receive mabel as a new teamate. Don was a very intelligent horse and a real help to Aden in starting these fillies. Don passed away in the Summer of 93.

The work sleigh is parked at a 45 degree angle to the fence so that the teamster can work safely around the team. Rita Freeman is holding Don while Aden brings Mable out. The position of the sled in respect to the fence is important to Aden's system.

The fence rails are all reinforced to handle the young horse being tied there.

D. Aden is leading Mabel out for her first time hitching.

E. (Above right) Here Aden has tied Mabel to a good strong fence post with the neck rope inside of the halter. A second lead rope goes from Mabel's halter to Don's hame tug ring. (In a western harness it is the billet at the tug.) The cross lines are now fastened. And then the neck yoke is put up. Aden has fastened the neckyoke so that it cannot accidently slide off the tongue. And then Aden takes Don's line down and runs it back to the sleigh stake on Mabel's side.

You might notice that this harness is quite different from what predominates in the U.S. This style is quite common to Eastern Canada.

F. Note how second lead rope is tied to Don's hame tug (billet) to help hold Mabel from getting around ahead of Don. Also note that lines are buckled into Mabel's bit.
G. Here Aden hooks all four traces, doing Mabel's last. Note Don's line on sleigh stake.

H. Mabel's line is taken down. Always keep lines to Mabel's side.
I. Both horse's are untied and Aden is on the lines. He drives Don, the trained horse, away from the fence. Don is on the inside of this turn.

229

J. (Above Left) Mabel's first trip around the field she's accustomed to. That is Ruth riding along.

K. (Above Right) Don and Mabel were brought back and tied to the fence. This gets mabel used to standing.

L. (Center) Notice how lines are looped to come undone quickly.

M. (Right) Third time Mabel was hitched a log was added to pull this added a little more lug after she had learned to drive.

Aden said that sometimes that first trip can be pretty fast but he keeps them going in a circle until the trainee slows down and stops.

N. (Above) This is Daisey (two and a half year old Belgian filly and full sister to Mabel) with Don. This is Daisy's second winter to be hitched. Daisy can now be hitched without tieing her. Aden believes you should never stand in front of the horse, always to the side.　　O. (Above right) Daisy's line is ready to be undone. Note where the helper is standing.

P. (Right) Hooking Daisy & Don to one log. Note: Helper is holding onto Daisy.　　Q. (Below) Letting the horses catch their breath & teaching Daisy to stand. Always keep lines handy & always use a dash board on sleigh.

R. (Above) Adding second log to Daisy & Don about the third day later. This adds more load to teach mare to draw (pull) very gradually.

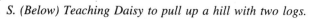

S. (Below) Teaching Daisy to pull up a hill with two logs.

T. Daisy hitched with Ted and on a different side. Ted is a fourteen year old Belgian gelding. Here Aden is teaching Daisy to stand with someone hanging onto lines while he works around the horses. There are no snaps on Daisy's lines, only buckles.

U. Ted and Daisy again. Daisy gets used to working and the sound of wood being loaded. Note the helper at Daisy's head.

V. Daisy getting used to unloading wood. She is standing without a helper at her head but the lines are very close to the teamster's reach.

W. Hooking Daisy & Mabel together. Mabel is tied and the helper hangs on to Daisy while she's being hitched.

X. Daisy & Mabel just leaving the fence. Note that Daisy, the more trained horse, is used to move away from the fence. Daisy is also used to being on the opposite side.

Y. Daisy and Mabel being driven is the field. The mares went through repeat exercises on "Haw" - "Gee" -"Whoa" and "Stand".

And these two photos show the result. Both fillies alert, attentive, content and, below, enjoying being brushed. Many thanks to the Freeman family and to Mabel and Daisy.

Ray Drongeson's System

The late Ray Drongeson was my friend and mentor with the work horse business. And I would be sorely amiss if I didn't include a description of his training system. The problem is he didn't have any. He just did it. Ray had such a knack for, and sympathy with, horses that everything just seemed to work out. He worked a stallion and mares and one gelding. He raised foals and a couple of draft mules. When the foals came along he just spent a bunch of time with them because he liked to. I'd sometimes catch him in the barn hanging a driving harness on a month old filly, and smiling saying *don't she look a sight.* He'd take that filly out and tie her to her mother's side for a trip raking hay. She wasn't hitched but she did pack a mass of oversized harness and would keep Ray smiling at the look of it. Whenever one of his foals got to two or three years old he would like to hook them on the landside wheel position of a four-up pulling a sulky plow. It was more horses than he needed but he enjoyed driving the four-up and figured this way the youngster didn't have to work so hard. If I was pressed to describe Ray's approach I have to say it was a combination of reaction and get-it-done. He was a master at reacting to a situation that might have easily turned into a wreck but which he made into a little training triumph. He was also a straight ahead person who decided a job needed doing and just figured out how to get it done. And he seldom did things the same way twice. But the real key was that he loved his horses and treated them royally and they in turn loved him. The result was that just about anything Ray wanted to try with the horses turned out just fine. I miss him.

Summing It Up

I started this training book by saying that I like to believe I'm on the side of the horse. Yes, I did set out to try to help people train horses but it was because I thought I might be able to help the horse best by helping the people who choose to work it. I still believe that, but I am afraid, after more than five years of effort with this book, that I took on a mighty big project. I am sure there will be value found in this book, but I am concerned that it may have fallen short of my original goals. If so it falls short for two reasons. First because it is a difficult, sometimes illusive, subject. And second because what little information I've been able to gather and present may actually result in more confusion. I sincerely hope not. The thought of that haunts me, but the truth is the fear/concern never grew large enough to stop this project. I still do believe that we will improve with more knowledge and a wider spectrum of possiblities. And I am pleased to have taken the opportunity to pound away, on these pages, the message that the horse is a sublime, intelligent, passionate, powerful creature who is willing and available to aid us. And that the character of his aid is fully in our own hands.

So in passing I would ask of you a set of favors:

Please be care full and careful with all that you do around horses.
Please trust your instincts and doubt your fears.
Please trust and accept your horse(s).
Please be confident.
Please be willing to admit that you may not know how much you don't know.
Hookup with folks who are successful at doing what you want to do.

Buena suerte and good work, L. R. Miller

Bud Dimick (foreground) and L. R. Miller mowing hay on Singing Horse Ranch

TRAINING TEAMSTERS

By L.R. Miller

Table Of Contents

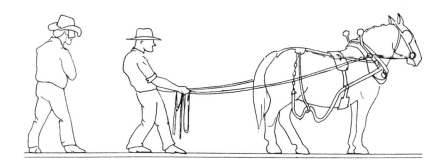

INTRODUCTION

This book is about teaching people how to drive horses for work and pleasure. The information is offered because I believe in the use of horses and mules in harness as a power source. It's a system which is practical, sensible, beautiful, self-renewing, non-polluting and efficient. And as a system it offers a power source that is readily available to people of any class. It is not elitist. It's a populist power source rooted in self-sufficiency and capable of show-casing great humanity and independence all at once. And it is humane, if the teamsters are well schooled as to best methods: Methods which give optimum results while providing comfort, exercise, useful work and pleasurable challenge to the horse(s) working in partnership. And that points to the true over-riding goal of this writing: I put this book together - first and foremost - for the horses and mules because they deserve an opportunity for a comfortable, healthy, long-lasting, working environment. The better they are handled, the better they will work. They will be handled better by people who take the time to understand the horse and the dynamic of its work in harness.

Jess Ross and Justin Miller with Molly and Queenie on the Singing Horse Ranch.

The author taking a break from the buck rake.

Today the sympathetic, yet uninitiated, person senses that working horses has a pace, style, and rhythm which is satisfying in ways which are difficult to measure. And that person is correct in that suspicion. It is wonderfully satisfying. But these same people, while seeing a craft which appears so natural and easy, are actually discovering something frightening, awkward, illusive, and demanding. I want to show them that just the other side of the problems they will rediscover their initial observation of natural ease. It is for these "new" people that I see a need to offer assistance and access to the mysteries of working horses.

Teaching people to be able to drive horses in harness has been a good and comfortable part of my adult life. I have long struggled, however, with the concept of a book on the subject. Struggled because I fear the result if a "green" person were to mis-read an animal (or this book) and find themselves in the path of harm and trouble. But my concern for the animals, my friends the animals, decided the need for this book.

Each failed beginning with the teamster's craft has included at least one disastrous experience for no less than one horse or mule. An experience that should not have happened. One which we might have prevented. So I presume to attempt to help the animals, and perhaps a few would-be teamsters as well, with this admittedly crude presentation of how the great craft may be understood and mastered. Another way it might be put is to say that the goal of this book is to help to teach people how to drive horses so that the horses might better enjoy safety, comfort, and freedom from fear in a working partnership.

244

But writing a book on a subject so full of subtlety, cultural variety, mystery and hidden complexities is difficult. I believe, though I pen these words, that no one can "learn" the craft of teamster from a book alone. The student must be guided by the clear understanding of being there. This craft is a thing which must be learned through experience and tutelage. You need your hands on the lines and a person by your side helping to guide and interpret. With book alone there is always the element of the reader's myopia, "accepting" only what he or she wants to read. Or seeing only what she or he wants to see. The author has some access to hyperbole, exaggeration, and metaphor to state a particular case for caution. But the reader may not want to hear this alarm and so just moves on into hazard's garden. The author cannot be there to admonish, warn, praise, and redirect. However, with an able tutor in tow there is much less chance of the student making a needless mistake.

Further reading of this text plus the companion writing on training workhorses should provide ample illumination of the fact that any new working relationship with horses or mules serves up uncountable variations of cause and effect, push and move. No writing could ever describe them all.

The written word might put the student into a described circumstance but it will not give complete understanding, and it cannot guarantee the most effective eventual perspective. Perhaps even a tutor or instructor cannot do this but they can prevent unnecessary accidents and adjust for mechanical misunderstanding.

Some readers will find reason to criticize the slow, tedious and seemingly trivial pace of the learning program outlined in this writing. Years of teaching workhorse workshops have repeatedly demonstrated to me how critically important it is for the individual to acquire through repetition (no matter how silly or simplistic the learning environ) a "vocabulary of response" married to a knowledge of what the equine might do in most situations.

Imagine with me please; the harnessed horse steps (maybe even jumps) sideways, head turned hard towards that from which he tries to escape. He snorts - tries hard to focus and swings his back end so that he can back straight away. He prepares himself to spin and run away. All this while you, with lines in hand, do what? Expect what? What you might expect comes best from your acquired knowledge and that from repeated practice. What you might do comes best from that "vocabulary of response" which, if you are ever to be a good teamster, will become a part of your intuitive nature. Like walking or riding a bicycle.

I have found that, without exception, the very best way for someone to learn to drive horses is in a concentrated workshop environment with several students, more than one instructor and at least two teams of horses. The reason this is a superior learning environment is because it multiplies the possible variables of experience and situations to engage in and witness. Often what we cannot grasp by actual effort becomes clear to us when we watch another person struggle with it or conquer it.

But not everyone can attend a workshop, or find a suitable tutor. And those people, should they choose to proceed alone (as I once did), may need some help. So, with some hesitation and concern, I offer this writing, these illustrations, and these photos in hopes they will help.

On another, parallel note: The years of workshops have demonstrated that some people are not suited to work horses. This does not mean that there is a type or size of person who cannot learn the craft. Anyone can. It means that there are people of certain temperament, anxiety level, cultural expectation, and/or attitude who will quickly discover they don't like working horses. As you might expect - of those who are attracted to this "way of going" most are suited. In fact many are "naturals" taking to the craft, in all its subtlety, as though they had done it all their lives. Those who are unsuited for the work horse should take up some other craft. The horses don't need them. While on the flip side, many of those who are "natural" and take to the craft easily will be a boon to the welfare of the working horse.

Learning how to drive horses is a challenge. Teaching the craft may be a greater challenge. I hope this book helps in some small way.

Bud Dimick mowing hay on Singing Horse Ranch

Chapter One

The Nature of the Craft

The briefest of historical notes

The art of driving horses in harness is a craft which has been with mankind, in limited forms, for several thousand years. However, contrary to popular assumptions the widespread use of work horses in harness for agriculture, mining, road maintenance, etc., is a fairly recent and short-lived phenomenon (200+ years) restricted primarily to Europe and North America. The halcyon days of the work horse in North America covered a century and closed between the first and second world wars. The rapid development of improved farm tools, coupled with massive industrial production of cheap implements and unbridled native ingenuity, resulted, across the U.S. and Canada, in the most highly developed and efficient animal-powered

agricultural system the world has ever seen. Before World War I farmers knew years of prosperity the like of which has never returned. And the draft horse and mule were cornerstones.

During most of that time nearly everyone drove horses because they had no other option (unless they were very wealthy and had others do the driving). And yet most of those people could not be called able teamsters. Fact is, if it weren't for the natural capacities of the equine (both physical and mental) many of those people could not have accomplished a challenging day's work with driving lines in hand. Many a team "took care of" incapable, and sometimes cruel, teamsters.

The truly able teamsters often found themselves atop a rocking dusty stagecoach or in charge of a freight outfit where 4, 6, 8, or more animals needed to be guided in crowded cities and on treacherous roads and all by one individual. (Yes, this is the root of the word "teamster" as it is used today to commonly refer to freight truck drivers.) Certainly there were some great teamsters satisfied to stay on the farm and plow or spread manure. And indeed as tools, methods, and ideas developed, more and more opportunity presented itself for farmers to test their horsemanship skills. But overall the bulk of people who drove horses from 1830 to 1930 just got by as best they could.

In this day and age, with the curiosity-driven fascination modern folk have in the image of working horses, we have the interesting turnabout that finds more people learning to be good teamsters and truly appreciating their craft, perhaps to a degree seldom felt 100 years ago.

Ontario, Canada, teamster John Male at a Work Horse Workshop

Dynamics and Mechanics

But what is the true nature of this craft? It is so easy to fall into the trap of seeing this as man cruelly subjecting beast to bondage and hard labor pulling implement or vehicle. Not to suggest that hasn't happened. But it is an unfortunate and limited view of something which has the great potential of being a richly rewarding and wholly comfortable labor of craft.

Instead, look to the specifics of the system. One or more horses, outfitted in straps and connecting hardware, are asked to pull tools or goods. And a person, usually from behind the animal, holds two or more leather ribbons (lines) which connect to metal bars (bits) the horses hold in their mouths. If this system is to work properly the person (teamster) asks the horses to move ahead, back up, turn or stop and the horses comply. The lines are used to turn the horses and, if necessary, remind them that a stop or backing is requested. Sounds so simple, yet ...

Within the dynamic of a team of horses and a teamster there are some dimensions and realities which need to be understood if the larger nature of the craft is to be appreciated. Work horses can weigh from 700 to 2,500 pounds each, whereas teamsters might reasonably weigh from 100 to 250+ pounds. Horses are mammals which evolved in a predator syncopated grazing environment. Survival belonged to those animals strong enough, bright enough and fast enough to run away when threatened. People in most western cultures are no longer subjected to such harsh evolutionary pressures. The result is that we have many people who

Mel Anderson, Washington teamster and his American Shires.

are slow, out of physical condition and dull-witted. (What might that suggest to one who believes in the idea of "survival of the fittest"?)

If two tons of alert, anxious, angry, or frightened horses decide to run away how can a disconnected, slow-to-react person hold them or argue the case? If those same two draft horses decide they will not move, how may that insignificant relatively weak human force them to? The scales are obviously, on the surface, tipped in favor of the horses unless the human can marshall understanding and develop a mutually trustful relationship. The only way the system, or relationship, can work properly (which is to say to its fullest potential) is if the horses willingly comply with operational requests. Herein is where the subtlety, poetry and mystery lays. Success, in the best sense possible, comes not from brute force but from understanding and acceptance.

But it must be said that a measure of success with working horses is regularly had by those clever enough to figure out effective measures for forcing submission. And those same people are often very cruel and insensitive to their working animals. Trust, acceptance, kindness and understanding are not in the working vocabulary of these people. Horses are to be used. They are viewed as dumb beasts and expendable. With these people the tragedy is complete. It is tragic for the poor animals treated thus. It is tragic for the general reputation of the teamster's craft. And it is tragic for the cruel teamster because he will never know the great possibilities of a trusting work relationship with horses.

The world of working horses is more like the mastery of a musical instrument than the wielding of a sledgehammer.

The nature of this craft includes the mechanics and the dynamic as well as an important over-riding poetry.

The mechanics of western working procedures can be simply described in this fashion:

The horse, or horses, wear a harness which includes a means to attach to that which is to be pulled or pushed. The harness also includes bits and lines which directly connect the hands of the teamster to the bars of the horse's mouth. The harness may also include various means for securing a backing or braking system for wheeled vehicles.

The dynamics of the system might be described

in this simple way:

The push is pull.

A signal is communicated by the teamster (usually by sound) to the horse(s) and, if that is what is requested, forward motion results. With that motion the horse pushes its shoulder against the collar tightening the tug (or trace) thereby converting a push into a pull (if the tug is attached to a load).

If the horse is hooked or hitched to a wheeled vehicle this forward motion will, with pressure forward into the collar, result in the cart or wagon rolling ahead. If that same horse stops, proper hook-up or hitching will cause a definite commensurate stop of the vehicle. If that same horse backs up, he will cause the vehicle to back up, if it is so designed.

If the horse is hooked to a load that is to be drug across the ground (dead drag) the forward dynamic is similar. There is, however, no way to back the "dead drag" load by backing the animal.

There are specialized applications of horsepower, such as the use of the walking plow, which have properties and limitations that are unique to the tool and the work. However, the "push-is-pull" phenomenon is basically the same.

We don't want to get too complicated with this dynamics discussion because our purpose is to get you quickly to the business of driving. But it is important to state, in passing, that truly efficient use of horses in harness will only come if the teamster has a thorough grasp of all aspects of the dynamics of draft. Small adjustments can result in much lessened draft, ease of tool operation, more ground covered in a given time, and happier work mates.

Given this crude over-simplified description of the mechanics and dynamics we can briefly discuss a little of the poetry and intricacies of the teamster's craft. Briefly because the larger, more complete view of the subject is, of course, the goal and content of this entire volume.

I have stated that the craft is poetic and that this is important. Why are so many of us attracted to this work horse business? It is contrary to the modern cultural mandate for homage to ever higher levels of technological development. It is not for reasons of profit, fashion, or convenience that we feel drawn to the work horse. And I feel that neither is it an attraction to some nostalgic notion. We are attracted because the best examples of the craft provide us with a window to a place where a pace, rhythm, smell, sound and texture offer us a chance to feel good about ourselves and what we do. It is the cold-efficiencies of highest technologies versus abiding warmth and the connectedness of employed craftsmanship. It is a poetry that comes of allowing spiritual aspects to be a part of a working way.

What the good teamster is
What the good teamster does

The good teamster is always concerned with the health, comfort and general contentment of his horses.

The good teamster realizes he or she is an important part of a working whole. The teamster knows that good horses are the result of good handling, and that the good teamster is a result of understanding born of repeated successes.

The good teamster communicates with a soft voice and a positive attitude and the best expectation.

The good teamster always pays attention to all the little details and aspects of the work horse system thereby avoiding hazard and providing equine comfort.

The good teamster always looks for clever ways to have horses make the right choices by making the right thing easy and the wrong thing hard or impossible.

The good teamster has a healthy respect of the intuitive nature of the equine.

The rewards you may expect

Once you've acquired a working capability of the teamster's craft your first reward will be an indescribable sense of belonging to a world both new and old. The craft might give you self assurance and a piece of self-worth. This modern age strips us of most of the capacities, skills and experiences which go a long ways toward providing a natural sense of who we are and what we are capable of. As overblown as it may sound, something as simple as the ability to drive horses and accomplish work with them gives us back a direct sense of ourselves. The acquisition of the teamster's craft is a real antidote for inadequacy.

But there is another conceptual bridge to cross. One which can return bushels of measurable benefit. If you know how to work horses you still have to make the choice of whether or not to use them and your new skill.

You will find plenty of detractors who will argue against the idea and even ridicule it. But the suspicions you've experienced with the learning are to be trusted. Yes, you can farm with horses and mules - TODAY - and to great reward. The work can be done, done well, done in good natural time and done with amazing cost efficiency. It is your choice and you are half way there with the acquisition of the teamster's craft. The benefits are real.

Chapter Two

How to Begin to Learn

Workshops

The best place for you to learn to drive is in a hands-on workshop setting. The resurgent interest in draft horses, over the last 15 years, has accounted for the sprouting up of many clinics, seminars and workshops throughout North America. Most are of a presentation format. Some are of a hands-on format. Those that are <u>presentation</u> have students watch demonstrations and listen to presented materials. Those which are <u>hands-on</u> have students participate in exercises. Presentation formats may have their value. But it is my belief that the subtleties of the teamster's craft cannot be appreciated and learned without actual participation. For this reason I encourage you to research the format of any workshops you are

Aden Freeman drives the team while L.R. Miller helps a young novice plowman at a Canadian Work Horse Workshop in 1981. Photo by H. Holmes

253

considering and put a premium on the ones which give you hands-on time.

Beyond that there is a question of evaluation. How do you know if a given workshop is good for you or not? First off, I recommend that you look for workshops which focus on your ultimate interest. If you are interested in showing horses in harness - go towards the workshop with that focus. If your interest is working horses on a farm - go towards the workshop with that focus. Also, allow yourself to be suspicious and questioning. If a workshop instructor does not show horses how can he teach you to show horses? If the instructor does not farm with horses how can he show you the way? Also, work to understand <u>why</u> you are interested in workhorses and what sort of relationship you want. With that knowledge seek out a workshop and instructor which mirror your concerns. There are many ways to work horses and to teach working with horses. Your chances for success as a student/ graduate of a workshop are proportionately higher if you feel sympathetic with the philosophy of the instructors.

Why a workshop setting? As you will discover on these pages teaching yourself to drive horses will involve:

a. proper setting

b. instructional materials (i.e., this book)

c. proper animal(s)

d. right equipment

e. and preferably a knowledgeable helper.

A well conceived workshop should provide all of these, thereby reducing your cost and hassle. Plus there is the added advantage of a proper workshop's providing a "safe" environment to learn in.

It should be added that the teamster's craft is so subtle and complex that the best any workshop can do is to immerse the student in introductory experiences. You should not expect to come out of any workshop as a capable teamster. It will take practice and experience to fully develop your own "vocabulary of responses" to given situations and a working ease with the system. Workshops often provide an excellent beginning.

But workshops, by necessity, are expensive two ways. First, you have to pay for the course - often in the hundreds of dollars. Second, you need to find a block of time and travel to the workshop site. Although there are several, they are far flung enough that you should expect to have to travel some to get to your choice.

There is another option within the same perameters. That is to hire the time of an instructor. Before I discuss this option I would like to put in a plug for the real value of sharing the learning experience with others. It adds unique dimensions and breadth to your learning. Given the choice between some sort of collective learning experience and a private tutor opt for the group. If for no other reason than you can't possibly dream up all the good questions that might come from a dozen different students. The answers to those questions all go towards your own learning.

Instructors

If you can't do the workshop thing the next best route is to have someone teach you the business. There are some truly outstanding, even legendary, instructors scattered around North America. People like Ken Demers and Les Barden out New England way. And Dan Tatum from Texas. And Forrest Davis of Montana, and the list goes on and on. Some of them are professionals and some are just good neighbors anxious to help.

Just as there are a bunch of able instructors there are just as many working relationship formats between student and teacher. From formal for-cash courses, to neighbors helping out. I can't begin to suggest how or what to do or expect from such a plan or approach. But there are some observations and cautions I might offer.

As one who has farmed with horses for over twenty years I can tell you that no season passes without my receiving many offers from people to let me teach them what I know. Here's a sampling of proposals I have received from strangers (received and rejected):

"I'm willing to work for you on your farm on these terms: Room and board plus $5 per hour plus my choice of one of your workhorse mares in exchange for work from April through September. In consideration of this I expect that you will teach me all you know about working horses and farming." Charlie

"I don't have any farm experience but I'm high on learning how to work horses. For $7 per hour I'll work hard with the horses but you'll have to stay with me so I don't have any problems. I'm available from July 5 to July 21. Let me know immediately." Elizabeth

"I've watched old men do it. It can't be all that hard. So here's the deal: Let me build a cabin on a corner of your place, teach me what I need to know and give me one foal each year and you'll never have to clean your own barn again." Seth

"My wife will do the cooking. My kids'll help out. All we need's a place to squat for a year or so and some eats. You show me how and I'll work your horses. Sound like a deal?" Rapture

"$1,500 a month, a trailer hookup, half a beef a year and some instruction about draft horses and I'll manage your place." Sheila

I hope the above sampling sends a clear message. Something's out of whack. As a farmer I do not have the time to devote to the day-after-day "watching over" of a student who's

255

working animals I value hooked to equipment I prize covering land I've nurtured. You can't pay me enough to allow a green stranger this experience. So imagine my reaction to those who propose that I pay them handsomely for the privilege of teaching? And many other farmer teamsters feel likewise. The above might sound harsh but I feel it's important to include in this discussion because it points to a root cause of so many problems in the search for learning the teamster's craft. I am willing to admit that my perception of the problem may be slanted or perhaps even wrong. But the problem still does exist and, for many would-be students, needs to be addressed or understood. Otherwise many folks who should gain access to the learning process will find themselves shut out by their own attitude. I will take it one step further; I personally feel that a student who comes to this process with the arrogance to presume something is owed to him or her will find many unnecessary obstacles to education. Please understand this; if you want to learn how to work horses you are going to have to pay the price. Either in cash for formal instruction, or in some equitable, balanced trade. Or in your own perseverance or with cleverness. It won't happen for free.

But I don't want this to sound too one-sided. As editor of a magazine about farming with horses I receive calls and letters from people who feel I should mediate disagreements between students and instructors. Many a time I've heard stories of how people paid handsome sums of money to learn to drive horses and got little or no instructions for their pay.

Outside of formally applying to a generally recognized qualified instructor there is a common sense approach to getting good help.

In just about every nook and cranny of North America there are people working horses. That may come as a surprise to some of you. You might reasonably figure that since you haven't seen them there's nobody in your area. Fact is folks who work horses have often found it most comfortable to keep it to themselves if possible. We don't make any big noise in our small town about working our horses. But many folks know it. And the unfortunate truth is that some of those people ridicule us for working the horses.

All of this is to say that you are going to have to look for those people working horses in your area. Ask around, and don't get discouraged if the first answers are negative or silly. Keep asking. When you do finally locate someone who's working horses introduce yourself as someone who's interested but make no offers, no proposals. You don't want to scare off this potential resource, and on the other hand you don't want to commit yourself prematurely. Look around the place, at the animals and the equipment and judge if it's something that suits you. If you find yourself convinced that this teamster is lazy or sloppy or cruel why would you want him for an instructor? That's not to say your observations are correct. It's to say your instincts and feelings should be respected. Any person who might teach you should easily be respected. If, on the other hand you are delighted, impressed, intrigued and excited by the farm backdrop you witness allow yourself to conclude that, at the very least, you NEED to know these people who have shaped this place. And hope that you might earn their respect enough to warrant a conversation about learning from them. But, in my opinion, you should NOT "demand" anything because it will most likely close doors.

Once you've "discovered" people you consider good examples, role models and possible help to you in your learning, make certain you clearly communicate your interests and hopes. Then things might begin to happen. It may never evolve into a formal instruction but you will be learning from the beginning. Things said and not said, mannerisms, displayed expectations, obvious cautions and priorities will all be information available to you in a new and developing friendship with these teamster folk. Most important they will be there, just up the road, to lend a hand. That will mean a great deal to you a little later on. So try to be there for them. Offer to help with unrelated as well as teamster related duties and problems. Sure, you may not be skilled or knowledgeable. But that will be obvious - it is your help and willingness to help that will build the relationship. And it all has to start with a humble, honest, unpresumptuous introduction.

Perhaps, to some, the following list of cautions might seem repetitive or all to obvious but I offer them in the spirit of thoroughness. (These cautions might apply equally to paid instructors.)

When looking for good help and building a working relationship:

A. Look to the physical condition of the horses or mules, but keep in mind that you might not be a judge of whether good husbandry is being practiced. Even so, obvious evidence of abuse or neglect should cause you to back away from asking the responsible person for help.

B. Be wary of the stranger who claims to know everything and is anxious to give you your dream immediately. Something's wrong.

C. Do not be too discouraged by the person who might seem unfriendly, unenthusiastic, reluctant to answer questions and generally doubting. Your own enthusiasm and/or inquisitiveness could be difficult to take. If you recognize evidence of caution in the person it is a good sign. Your efforts in winning friendship could be richly rewarded.

D. Determine if you're speaking with the person or persons who are truly responsible for what you've found. Sometimes owners take ready credit for skills and accomplishments which do not belong to them. Or vice versa - employees lay claim to things that don't originate with them. You want to cultivate the person who cares for and drives the horses or mules. You want as friend the craftsman.

E. Don't give up on someone because their response to you is less than you expect.

257

Keep going back, be persistent but with a healthy respect for their time and space. Be kind and exhibit genuine interest in their skills.

F. Don't allow yourself the trap of too quickly feeling expert. Many a sharing and learning relationship has collapsed when the student started criticizing and doubting the teacher. Doubts and questions are healthy and you should respect your own. But you should also respect the fragile nature of the "learning" environment you've entered into and know that you are there because of your lack of knowledge. It's true of many things, and certainly no less so of the teamster's craft, that a little knowledge is a dangerous thing - and that a view of the whole forest is only available to the humble, attentive person who has traveled the complete distance across it.

G. Never pretend to know what you don't know. Within the world of working horses, nothing gets newcomers into more trouble than pretending (either to themselves or to others) to know when they don't.

H. Don't get too anxious. Prepare yourself to accept that it will take a good while to learn this subtle craft.

Learning By Working

It's not true but awfully easy to say: What better way to learn how to work horses than to get a job on a horse powered farm and acquire the skill by doing it? I happen to believe that either the workshop system or an instructor are better. The completely green individual, the one who knows nothing of the equine in harness, is a hazard to himself, the farm, the animals and the farm owner if allowed - after a brief explanation - to work horses in a farm environment. Too many things can go wrong. And, if a successful first day is completed, the worst possible message has been transmitted to the novice. You can almost hear him say, "Hey, that wasn't so hard."

If you aren't grounded in a solid understanding of the basics you are heading for a wreck.

But I am not saying that the idea of working on a farm, and honing skills, is wrong. Quite the contrary. Work on a horse powered farm can be an excellent environment to truly learn the vagaries and fine-tuning important to a full-time dependence on horsepower. And repetition, especially of good habits, builds a lasting foundation.

But the idea of farm work as instruction comes much easier to the student than to the farmer. Most farmers are not teachers, they are workmen. They do not have the time to spend to do an adequate job of showing someone how to harness and work horses. They can't afford to have good horses or mules hurt and equipment torn up.

Learning by working often means having to accept the full range of farm or ranch duties. It will seldom mean you get non-stop tutorial attention and work with the horses. There's forking to do as Sharon Ross demonstrates.

There are a few farmers who are good teachers and interested in having apprentices but their needs and expectations are in conflict with those of the student.

A short while ago I visited with a man who farms with horses and teaches people the craft. He shared with me this frustration.

"After careful thought we take someone on because we feel they have the ability and aren't afraid of work. We house them, feed them, teach them all we know and pay them for their work. And each time we have the same problem. Just when they "think" they know work horses they want to leave. We try to tell them there's much more to learn but they think they know it all.

"You see, when they first come we tell them it takes at least a year's commitment. And we explain that their work isn't worth much to us until they are at least knowledgeable enough to be let alone with the horses. And that's the point when they say they have to move on. It's a waste for us because all that time teaching goes when they go. And it's a waste for

them because we know that they won't be able to handle the horses when they are truly on their own."

My suggestion is that the beginner gather the best introduction possible from workshops, instructors and instructional materials and THEN seek out a farm to hone that into true skill. At that point he or she has something to offer the farmer in the way of usable skills and service. And, with the basics secured under belt, the student can get on with the higher learning from experience that will build confidence and craftsmanship.

Learning On Your Own - Books

A friend of mine, who worked horses, once threw at me that "cliche" as insult: "People write how-to books because they can't do the thing themselves." Simplistic though it may be there is some truth in the caution. It is dangerously easy for a book to appear correct, though it may not be. And often, vice versa, the skilled craftsman cannot communicate in letters.

I know I'm far more successful with my horses and as a teacher than I ever will be writing books. With the horse work and the teaching I can be responsive. With the writing I'm forced to be simply reflective. Working my horses is pure joy for me partly because every situation calls for a unique response. Same is true with teaching. With writing there is little or no room for responding and lots of worrying about whether or not everything's been covered properly. All this is an attempt to say what has been said before: The best of books - the most earnest and capable authorship - does not/can not replace "being there" for student and teacher.

Written material, as instruction, is always dangerous because there are so many ways the reader can interpret a written description of a procedure, adjustment, warning, maneuver or situation. For this reason it lies with the reader/student to protect his or her self with the complete determination that what is read is understood. When dealing with written instructorial material exaggerated caution is wise.

So if you choose to go solely with a book or books (this one included) please know that "you are on your own." I cannot recommend to you learning the teamster's craft from a book. Books can be very helpful but my strongest recommendation is for you to have a capable teamster (whether a teacher or not) with you as you work with the horses. If you choose to use a book (this one included) there is certainly no problem employing the assistance of a capable teamster who might happen to disagree with the author's approach. Better you should have a safe beginning with lots of disagreement than a disastrous wreck where all were in agreement.

Most instructional books are straight forward boiled-down presentations of one approach towards learning the subject. At the risk of building a burdensome boring volume

I have deliberately chosen to present a complex and inclusive view of these two subjects I see so keenly related. *Training Workhorses/Training Teamsters* is an honest effort to acknowledge and showcase a great deal of work, by many people. For this reason this book may be awkward and too broad for the anxious would-be teamster. Such a person might be better served by an illustrated pamphlet covering a fast track approach to the basics. But I doubt it because the subtlety of the craft cannot be avoided. It will, at some point, force the beginner to make a commitment to learn it all or give up.

Before leaving the subject of books I need to add, in what might seem like a bit of a contradiction, that the written word is as important an element in the trail of human history as any monument or artifact. In fact, some might say more so. So I see the responsibility of compiling this work on animal power as a solemn one. Should there ever come a time, as almost was and we hope never returns, when the employment of the horse or mule in harness is a far distant memory, books such as this will be an important record of a human skill. A record we may have some constructive need of. Especially if we need to reach for craft to aid in survival. And certainly the venomous cultural permeations of corporate ethics and ever-higher technologies guarantee humanity's return to previous evolutionary states. Who knows, perhaps some future perfect secret society of Luddite Teamsters will circle their wagons repeatedly around the cellular walls of evil corporate headquarters till they render it all to butter! And to do it we will need books!

Back to learning the teamster's craft: It is possible, even probable, that a workshop instructor and a book (such as this one) will still not give you all the information you want and need. You will need to know about care and feeding, possibly about equine reproduction, about harness variations for odd jobs and maybe even some advanced horse psychology. This text assumes you have done your background homework on the essentials of HORSES. Other books are available and we recommend the ***Work Horse Handbook*** as a companion volume. But do not neglect other sources of information including the various opinions and observations of differing yet successful teamsters.

Animals As Teachers

You can't be around the world of teamsters long before you'll hear reference to how this or that horse or mule was a good teacher. And it's certainly true. It points, once again, to my long held belief that horses are intelligent creatures whose minds work in ways we can sometimes only guess at.

The ***Training Workhorses*** half of this text deals directly and indirectly with the subject of horses as "teachers" to other horses.

In this half of the book we need to mention about horses as teachers of teamsters.

As a beginner or novice you should put the highest premium on access to, or ownership of, the quietest best trained horses you can find. It doesn't matter what size, color

A knowledgeable horse can be as good a teacher and often far more forgiving that a human tutor. Phil Taft drives Cali and Lana on the mower and L.R. Miller stumbles along behind.

or breeding they are. It may come as a surprise to some to read that it doesn't matter what age they are either. (I have had many an occasion to handle horses 20 years and older which were ill-tempered, poorly trained and prone to calamity. By similar token I have had the pleasure to work with, and train, 2 and 3 year olds which were made sweet tempered, well-trained and prone to success.)

The woods are littered with the debris from wrecks which were caused by the foolish insistence of beginners for "just the right color size breeding gender and flash" in their first team. I know first hand. My beginning, laced with arrogance, impatience, and the dangerous refusal to admit my own naivete had tragic results. Turning my education around took time, help and great patience. I had to back up from a pair of purebred mares to a mismatched crossbred team of Nevada mongrels before I even began to get a clue of what driving horses was about.

If your initial learning experience is in a hands-on workshop, or with a schooling situation where horses are provided, you are in luck. If the animals have any serious shortcomings, in the protected, guided workshop environ you can use those for their lesson value and leave it all behind when you go. Not so if you are alone at home with your problem animals.

Learning the teamster's craft requires a balance of many elements.

It can be difficult for people to learn. But if forced to begin with poorly trained, ill-tempered beasts the learning process becomes impossible. Yet at the risk of confusing you it is very important to add that <u>no</u> horse is "fool" proof. As an intelligent determined student you "should" have the opportunity to work safely and <u>properly</u> with a well-trained animal or animals. But keep in mind that the well-trained animal "should" have the similar guarantee of never being required to work with or for a "heavy-handed," loud, abusive, stupid, impatient, and insensitive human. And further more the well-trained horse or mule should not suffer the unnecessary cruelty of having to "teach" the novice without knowledgeable help close by.

I cannot begin to list the infinite variety of possible dangerous circumstances that the unschooled individual might subject a horse to in an effort to learn driving or get some job done. A quiet well-trained horse might ignore or excuse many of these mistakes. It might even have the sense, as many of them do, to refuse to proceed until the errors have been corrected. But imagine what a frightened inexperienced animal or a clever mean-spirited animal might do with such a situation?

Jumping ahead a little bit to illustrate the point of horses as teachers: As a student it will be difficult to fit it into your nervous perspective but I must insist you remind yourself repeatedly to "read" your horse(s). Learn the signs they send and watch for them. Watch the ears. Watch the elevation of the head. Watch the back. Watch the breathing. Watch the walking. Watch everything. Teach yourself to know signs of fear, comfort, fatigue, illness, alertness, lameness, discomfort. With the quiet, well-trained horse the signs are more various

A learning scene at the last Small Farm Gathering in Holden, Missouri.

263

and often more subtle than with others. But they are so important to know. Because it is in these ways that the horse begins to speak to you. If you are to be a good student you have to "hear" the teacher. You have to understand the "teacher." As you develop the ability to read your horse(s) something miraculous begins to happen: The horse recognizes the signals you return and makes a judgement of you. If the horse appreciates your response it begins to accept you. If it does not appreciate your response it rejects you. Far fetched? No. Imagine this circumstance: You notice from your horses working posture (she leans a certain direction) and her ears (they move back and forth but lay mostly back in a pose of irritation) that something's not right. You stop and check her and, running your hand under her collar you discover a stiff weed stalk stuck in the stitching in such a way as to jab her neck. You remove it, massage her neck, and proceed. She works better, more comfortable and has had a clear indication that YOU relieved her discomfort. She returns the favor by an almost imperceptible increase in her willingness to do as you ask. With time such occurrences result in an intangible but powerful bond the result of which is often mistakenly perceived as better training. Whereas, in truth, it is the evidence of a greater friendship and a finer working partnership. So it is that the largest part of the mystery of the teamster's craft boils down to genuine reciprocal caring.

So the animals teach us that we must be prepared to give if we are to get results. If we are to learn we must understand the lessons that are given and act upon them.

Proper Setting & Equipment

Once again, if you are enrolled in a workshop or school the package you buy should include the proper setting and equipment.

But if you must do this thing on your own here are some suggestions that will certainly help you.

The ideal setting would include a round pen enclosure preferably 40 feet across with a fence height of at least 4 feet. It should be a true circle with no corners. There should be at least one gate 10 feet wide. If this is not possible a fenced pen of 1000 square feet of area will work.

Next it would be luxuriously handy if a 5 to 10 acre pasture, preferably level or gentle gradient, were available. However, a dry lot of 1/2 acre or more would also work fine. In the absence of either a secluded road with no, or very little, vehicular traffic would suffice. If no space is available to you, you may have to haul your animal(s) and gear to a suitable spot. Check into neighboring horse arenas that might be available to you for an hour or two. But by all means DO NOT attempt to learn to drive in a setting which has many hazards and complications. For example, do not attempt to learn driving in your house yard with laundry on the line, dogs running loose and children playing in the corner. Use plenty of common sense and give yourself the benefit of a space to work that is free of distractions, hazards, risks and obstacles. You will have plenty on your mind so why not start with the score card in your favor?

Later the reasons for the described settings will become apparent.

As for equipment the list would include:
Good strong suitable harness that fits properly (see illustration)
A solid single tree with a detachable hook (see illustration)
A solid double tree if two horses are to be used (see illustration)
A solid neck yoke if two horses are to be used (see illustration)
A forecart (see illustration)
A suitable 4-wheeled vehicle/wagon
A sled or stoneboat (see illustration)
Two logs or rails 10 to 16 feet long and 4 to 8 inches in diameter
6 to 8 feet of chain with a slide hook (see illustration)
2 - 30 foot lengths of clothesline rope (or facsimile)
4 rubber pylons or mid-sized rocks
A child's tricycle (see illustration)
Two electric fence spring gate handles (see illustration)

The reason for all of the items will be apparent as the exercises unfold. But something must be said of the qualities noted.

As for the harness: "Good" and "strong" refer to the materials used being properly measured and cut plus properly dressed and sewn. And the connecting hardware being solid and appropriate for the job at hand. If the harness used is older harness take great care that the leather is neither raggy (comes of oiling old brittle harness) and prone to tear or rip. Or that the harness leather stitching is rotten and not able to hold much pressure. Or that the leather is so dry and cracked that it will simply fall apart under pressure. If you do not feel competent to judge the quality of an old harness DO NOT USE IT until you have a knowledgeable person judge its condition.

As for the newer nylon and biothane harnesses similar cautions should be used. The material might be less likely to break but stitching, workmanship, and design remain important. One added note: With some synthetic harness sharp edges at key wear points can cause irritation and even abrasion to the working horse.

The proper fit of the harness is an important lesson for the would-be teamster. Rather than tie up this text with the particulars an illustration is offered, but I recommend you read the companion text the **Work Horse Handbook.** For the initial ground driving exercises presented here the perfect fit of collar and harness is less critical. But a work horse or mule cannot be expected to push a load against its shoulder and respond properly to line pressures on the bit if the harness is improperly fitted.

The equipment list makes simple reference to "solid" hitch gear. These items are regularly available in steel and in wood. No recommendation is given one over the other. But common sense dictates that these items be free of rot, bends, tears and breaks. In other words, they should be amply strong for the work they will perform. Should a single tree or connecting clevis (shackle) break while you are trying to understand how to drive, the animal's reaction may render your lesson environment worthless - or worse.

If you feel uncomfortable assessing the quality of harness and hitch gear get knowledgeable help.

As for the sled, forecart and wagon; these are recommended specifically for driving exercises. You can get by okay with either a forecart or a wagon. But you should have a stoneboat or sled of some type. Since your future with work horses may be somewhat uncertain, at least the facts of how you will use them, it might be wise to attempt to borrow some of this equipment. A sled can be built easily enough and with a little shop skill so can a forecart (plans for both appear in the **Work Horse Handbook**).

The remaining items on the list will make some sense as we proceed.

Duke

PYLON

ROCK

ELECTRIC FENCE
GATE HANDLE

LOG CHAIN

SINGLE TREE

SWIVEL
GRAB HOOK

NECK YOKE

DOUBLE TREE

267

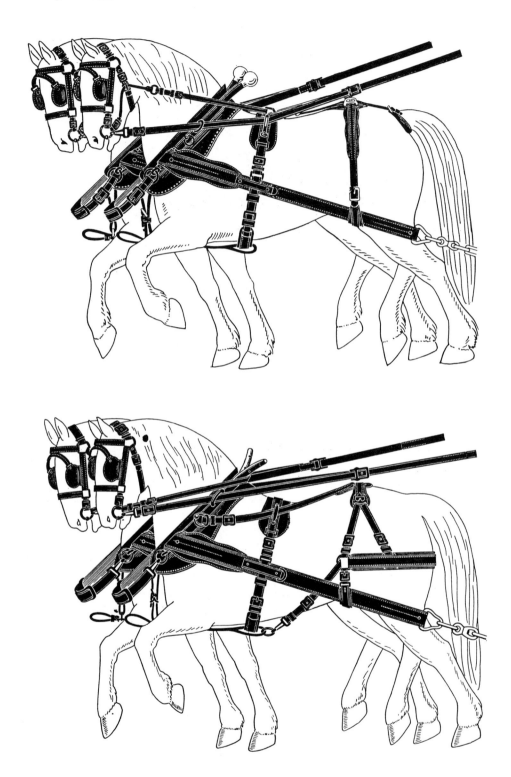

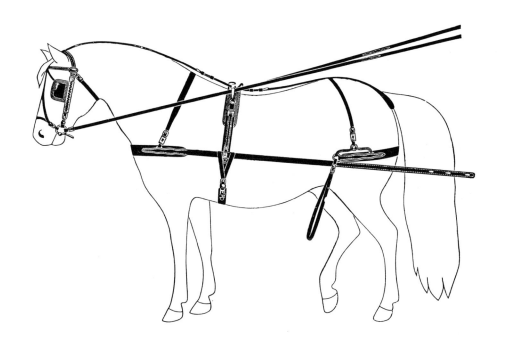

SINGLE STRAP PONY HARNESS

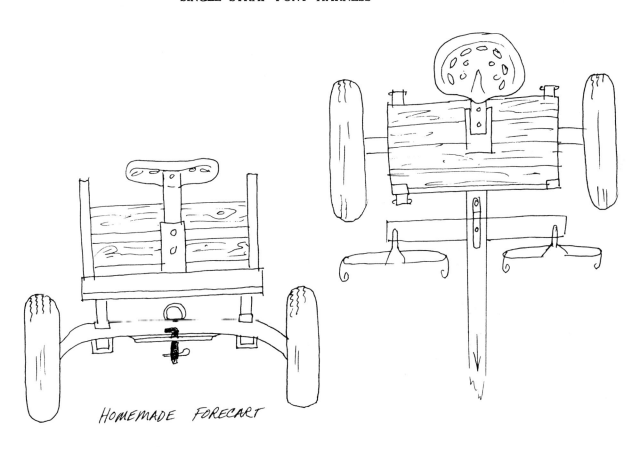

HOMEMADE FORECART

269

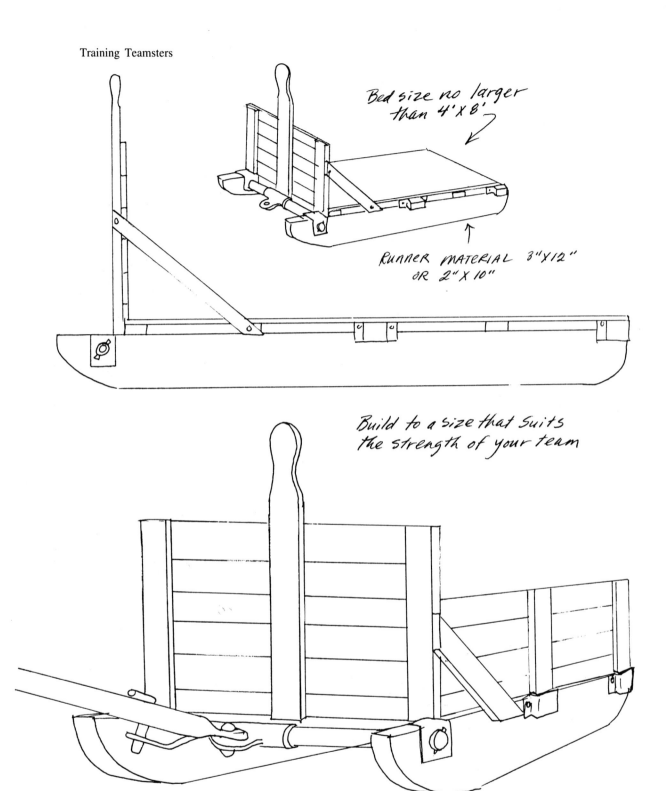

Bed size no larger
than 4' x 8'

Runner material 3"x12"
or 2" x 10"

Build to a size that suits
the strength of your team

STONEBOAT OR WORKSLED

Chapter Three

Driving Dynamics

From Hands to Lines to Bit

As we discuss the dynamics of driving I'll offer some exercises which will get you immediately started towards learning experiences. All this information is offered with the assumption that we both want the same result. That result is to develop (and honor) a working relationship between teamster and animals which allows for the widest and most fluid range of maneuverability and a comfortable partnership. We are shooting for mutual acceptance and respect.

From the outside and to the casual, uninitiated observer it may seem all too obvious that the person driving the horses is hanging on to them by way of those long leather reins [sic] attached to their heads ... It's not quite that way.

In what we refer to as conventional North American harness horse use, the horse carries a metal bar (of various design) called a "bit" comfortably in its mouth. To both exposed outside rings, or ends, of this bit are attached two long separate leather "lines" which travel

271

back, often through "guides" on the harness, to the teamster's hands.

Simply and ideally put, through various light pressures on these lines the teamster communicates the desired responses to the animal(s). Forward motion, backing, and turning are at times communicated through the lines.

However, and this is very important to you and germain to this author's approach to working horses, the lines should always function as a critical but secondary communication tool with the animals. Understood voice commands are the most important tool. More on this later.

Perfect Tension

For many years now I've referred to the desired line pressure for driving as "perfect tension." I've never been completely happy with this term but none has sprung to mind that works better to describe the necessity. Luckily, however, there are exercises and devices that do demonstrate the concept.

First allow me to attempt, once again, to describe, in writing, what is meant. As has been noted the harnessed horse carries a bit in its mouth. The bit is held in position by the headstall or bridle. For more detailed information on bit design and function see **The WORK HORSE HANDBOOK** and *TRAINING WORKHORSES* . When properly adjusted (see illustration) there is no discomfort. In the absence of lines or any other restriction the bridled/bitted horse can move its head freely from side to side.

Elementary to the early stages of training horses are those exercises which teach the animals to follow their heads in forward motion. (See Training Horses this volume.) By use of pressure on one side of the bit, and commensurate release of pressure on the other side, the horse's heads are turned in one direction. As they move ahead the body naturally finds comfort in following the head. Likewise, pressure equally distributed on the bit causes the thinking horse to back up in order that the pressure be released. In these ways bit pressure communicates desired movement, and can also send a variety of directives (i.e.; a light flick or jerk for "pay attention now," or "don't rub your bridle on your teammate.")

As you can see from the illustrations of bits and bit functions, great discomfort may greet the horse if the bit is improperly fitted or if excessive pressure is used. A bit fitted too tight will eventually cause sores and then a callous or deadening of the area. This totally destroys the mechanical effectiveness of the bit but much more important guarantees the horse's negative response to the situation and teamster. Likewise, excessive line pressure will also create a "hard mouthed" horse and destroy any good chance of subtle fine-tuned driving. All this will become increasingly apparent as we proceed. For now we need to establish that "driving" horses requires the mastery of perfect line pressure - not too light, not too hard - a perfect tension.

Proper position of the bit in a horse's mouth

LINE PATH ON
SINGLE
HORSE

Imagine with me, for a moment, that you had a steel bar affixed in your mouth with ropes attached to the ends and traveling back some 20 feet to a person's hands. A relationship has been established that has you proceed forward on voice command feeling with the sides of your mouth for some indication of what direction to go in. With a slight pressure right side (and a lessening of pressure left side) you turn your head to the right and your body follows. Now imagine that the bit is mercilessly tightened in bridle and/or that the person on the lines maintains a constant hard backwards pull - you, in such a case, would go from confusion to discomfort to anger quickly. So will a horse.

Learning the perfect tension, and the give-and-take that goes with smooth controlled turns takes practice and first hand successful experience. Happily we've devised ways of doing this without abusing horses in the process.

Devices and Beginning Exercises

The Dynamics of Driving the Single Horse

Please notice the illustrations which attempt to show, from top and side, where the lines pass and how they function on the single horse.

Your first exercise for learning perfect tension involves a pair of 18 to 20 foot long single driving lines (leather or nylon, if none available 1/4" rope will work as a rough facsimile) and those two spring-loaded electric gate handles we listed earlier. Tie one end of each gate handle to a barn wall or fence (as illustrated) about 6" apart. Now fasten the bit end of the lines to the remaining ends of the gate handles.

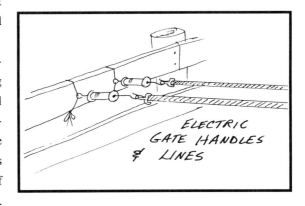

ELECTRIC GATE HANDLES & LINES

Back up the full length of the lines and pick them up holding as illustrated and pull back until the gate springs stretch. Now feel the spring and release the pressure to that point where the spring quits its stretch. Play with the lines until you can quickly and easily find that point of tension "just before the spring stretches." This is the tension you want to cultivate for driving horses.

As was said before, in making or directing a turn the bit's position in the horse's mouth is altered and the animal follows the angle change (see illustration). One of the most common frustrations at the early stages of learning driving comes with grasping, through practice, the concept of "defining the turn" with the lines. If you release all tension with one line and pull on the other the animal will likely swing quickly around in the direction of the slack line until

275

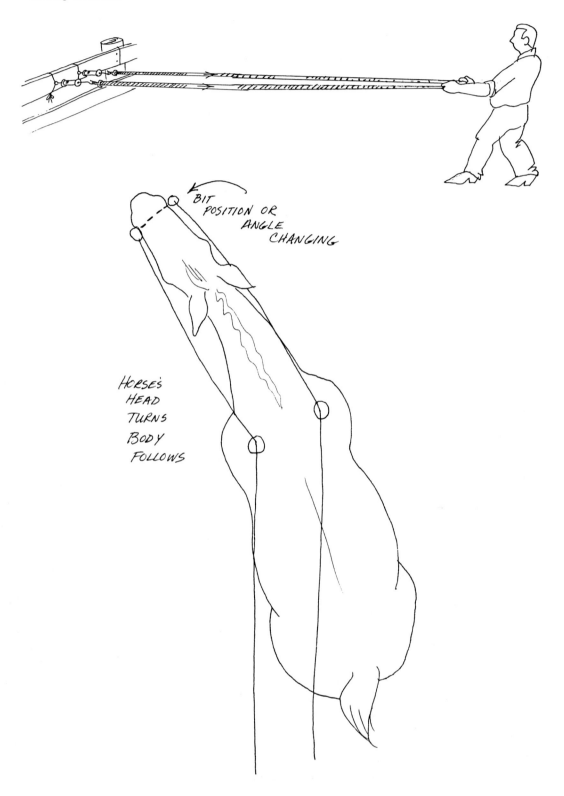

BIT POSITION OR ANGLE CHANGING

HORSE'S HEAD TURNS BODY FOLLOWS

facing you and you will have lost all mechanical or line control over the horse (more about this a little later). You need to learn the subtlety of making a perfect gradual turn through balanced line pressure. You need to learn to maintain equal pressure on both lines while changing the angle of the bit in the horse's mouth.

Once again I've come up with a little exercise which will spare the animal your steep learning curve.

Tie the ends of your 18 to 20 foot single driving lines to the ends of a tricycle's handlebars (see illustration & photos). Around the front of the trike fasten a short tow rope that does not impede the turning radius of the vehicle and ask someone to pull the trike while you hold the lines. Now try to turn the trike with the lines using an even pressure on both lines. This little exercise certainly demonstrates, in a hurry, how perfect tension is important even with turning.

You won't be ready to move on to the actual animal until you've mastered these two exercises. Too much slack in one or both lines translates to you "turning off" the line control of the horse. Too much pressure on the lines causes an abusive contest with the animal which will deny acceptance and deaden important and sensitive tissues and nerve ends of the horses. So practice with the devices. You should be able to turn the tricycle without having it fold up or rear up or fall over. It might seem silly now but it will pay big dividends in your learning process.

Good Hands Make the Team.

It's an old saying which carries much truth. Watch experienced teamsters that you admire and pay attention to their hands as they manipulate, hold and caress the driving lines. You are witnessing an

intuitive respect for the horse's abilities in general and his mouth in particular. That respect is repaid, many times over, by the working animal partner's acceptance and friendship. Abusive hands, on the other hand, create frightened, disrespectful, unfriendly, unproductive relationships.

Jess Ross on our three wheeled forecart at Singing Horse Ranch.

Learning How the Lines Work: **Driving** the Trike

A. If it helps any you can think of this tricycle by some name usually given to a horse, like Duke or Queen. A lead rope is wrapped around the yoke of the trike and single driving lines are fastened to the handle bars as shown.

B. As in this photo, have someone drag the trike while you take the lines in hand and steer a straight course.

D. ...fall over.

C. As in this photo, if you pull one line too much the trike will fold and ...

E. & F. A perfect tension on the lines will have the trike go straight or turn, as you direct.

278

G. Just as with a horse, it takes very little change to effect a smooth turn. But it does require even tension.

H. If you have a "belly" in your lines, as in this photo, you will have no effective control and...

I. ...the trike will fall over as the front wheel turns. You must maintain even tension on both lines.

J. However, if you pull back too hard "Duke" will rear up...

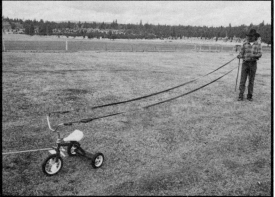

K. ...and fall over. And pulling back even harder only makes the situation worse. Imagine the handlebars as a bit in a horse's mouth.

L. Arms ahead of you and maintain an even tension on both lines and you will, as Tony Miller has, master the trike and be ready to move on to the horse.

The Dynamics of
Driving a Team of Horses

Please note the illustrations which attempt to show, from top and side, where the lines pass and how they function with two horses working side-by-side as a team. This arrangement is sometimes difficult to fully comprehend when first seen so please allow me some additional explanation. As the diagrams illustrate team lines look like a Y with one continuous "main" line and an adjustable short cross check line. In the North American harness system we're speaking about, the right side long "main" line passes from the teamster over the withers (see **Work Horse Hand Book** for anatomy) of the horse and through the top ring on the hame (see harness diagrams on page 72 & 75 of this text) and on to fasten to the bit on the right side - and the outside of the team. The cross check from that line passes over the withers and through the top hame ring of the same horse before crossing over to fasten to the right side (or inside) bit ring of the left horse. This entire procedure is repeated with the left line as its main portion passes over to the left side (outside) of the left horse and the cross check passes through the top inside hame ring and across to the inside of the right horse. It may sound confusing so please refer to the diagrams as you read the text. Also note in the diagrams that there is a definite geometry to how the team lines function. Proper adjustment is important. And, again, perfect tension in driving is critical if your working partners, the horses, are to clearly understand your wishes.

Your exercise to learn the functions of team lines involves a light driving double tree (i.e.; a buggy or carriage evener). If you don't have one readily available you can put something together from scraps of wood, which will work fine (see team line exercise evener diagram).

With a big spike fasten your evener to the top of a post (as illustrated) and attach the ends of your team lines as demonstrated. The evener should swing freely on the spike. Now back up to the ends of the lines and pull back gently and evenly watching what happens to the evener. Try to see it as the facsimile of bits in the horses mouths. Pull one line and let the other go slack and see what occurs. Now work to "turn" the evener with the same pressure on both lines.

Play with this exercise until you feel you understand the function and how just the right pressure on the lines makes everything work.

The Angles of the Lines When a Team is Straight and Turning

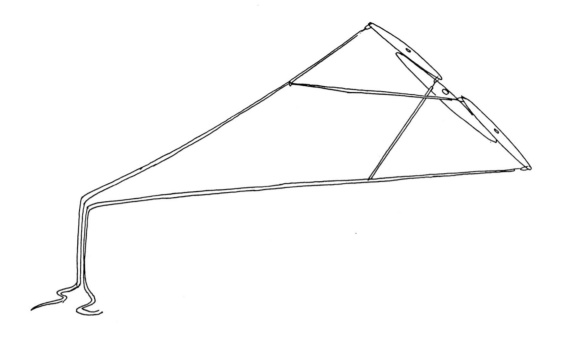

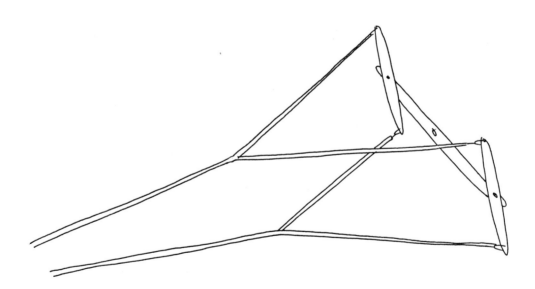

Team Line Exercise Evener

Chapter Four

First Time Driving

The Preliminaries

Now we finally get to the real stuff. Bear with me as I repeat some concerns.

You should not be learning to drive a horse or horses which are untrained. After you have learned to drive trained horses you may be of some constructive value to the green animal. Going in as an inexperienced person to try to teach and learn simultaneously places all involved in hazard's path.

You should have someone with you who at best knows the craft, and at the least is able to offer a hand to avoid calamity. Make sure it is a person who is physically fit and intelligent enough to remove themselves from a risky situation. That said you also need someone who is sure and calm enough to stay in the middle of things when it is safe and necessary.

If no one is available to you it becomes doubly important that you have done the exercises in the previous chapter and that the place you have to first drive in is perfect (description follows).

For your first driving experience you will be <u>ground driving</u> (that is to say the animals will not be hooked to any tool or vehicle and you will be walking behind while driving). You should be in an enclosed or fenced area. The ideal situation is a round pen or corral 30 to 40 feet across. If that is not possible a rectangular fenced pen or corral of approximately the same size will suffice. If you have neither, a paddock that is somewhat larger would work. You could also work inside of a barn but most such spaces are too cramped to give you a sense that you indeed are stopping and turning the animal(s). As was said before, do not attempt your first experiences in an environment which has many natural hazards and/or distractions.

I offer these cautions <u>NOT</u> because I believe the horse(s) will do something wrong. I offer these cautions because I worry that you, without qualified help in attendance will do something wrong which confuses or worries the horse(s) and that you are lacking in the experience and vocabulary of response to correct your mistake. I offer these cautions in an effort to protect the animal(s) and assure that you have a solid opportunity for a good beginning.

If you do not do as recommended, and you insist on working in a large unrestricted space, it should be understood that you might find yourself in a situation where the animal(s) decide(s) you are either frightening or not worth the effort. Should you loose control of the lead rope(s) and/or lines you may be left in the dust as the animal(s) runs off. In the recommended restricted area flight is nearly impossible. If, as you are learning, you cause the horse to run off you have allowed a dangerous precedent. The animal will remember that YOU frightened it and that he or she SUCCESSFULLY escaped YOU. When (and if) you catch the escapee(s) you may find a new, more complex, and difficult relationship exists between you. This is a situation you do not need when you're starting out to learn.

Driving the Single Horse - Beginning Exercises

What follows comes from the necessary assumption that the animal to be worked with is trained and experienced. If you don't already know the sound that is the starter switch, with a helper on the lead rope of the animal you are going to drive, experiment to determine what command works best to start the horse. There are many words and sounds used to train horses. What you use is not so important as the consistency. Always use the same word or sound. Now try out these most common ones while standing behind the handled horse: "Giddup," a whistle, a kissing sound, or a chirp. The animal should tell you which sound it is most used to. Remember this and use it when the verbal command to go is called for.

Harness your horse. If you need guidance refer to chapter four of the **Training Workhorses** portion of this text, or to the instructions in **The Work Horse Handbook.** Make sure the bit and bridle are properly fitted and that the driving lines are securely fastened to the bit. I recommend that you remove the snaps from the driving lines, if they have them, and buckle the lines direct to the bit. This might be helpful. If you are in a situation where a line should come unsnaped you might loose control of your horse.. The correct fit of the harness is not critical at this time because you will not be pulling anything. (Please refer to chapter four of *Training Workhorses*.)

Take the left line (as in diagram on next page) in your left hand between your forefinger and index finger. Take the right line in your right hand between the corresponding fingers. Remember your "perfect tension" and tricycle turning exercises. Now back up until there is very little slack in the lines (and so that what little slack there is in each line is the same). Now give the verbal command to go. As the animal steps ahead at a walk, just concentrate on walking directly behind and maintaining a perfect tension. Remember not too much slack nor too much tension. Now in a firm, calm voice say "WHOA" and prepare yourself to pull back on the lines if the animal does not stop.

If everything worked okay, congratulations! It was indeed a thrill, wasn't it? Now,

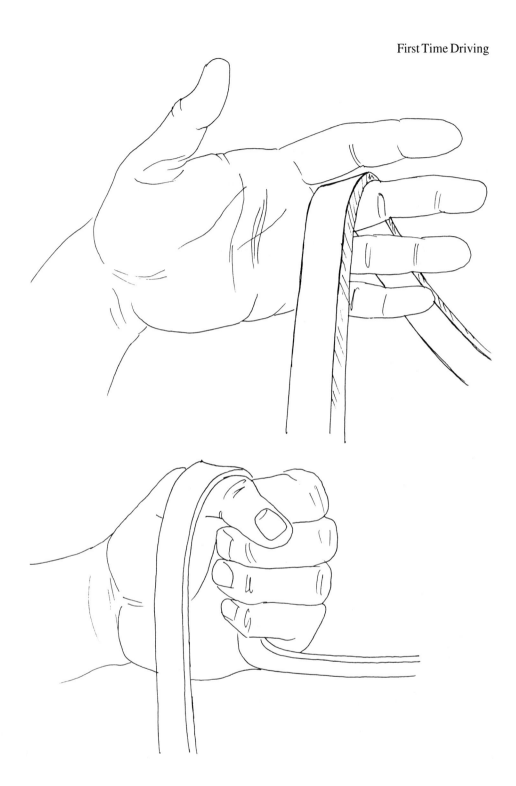

I suggest you hold the lines between you fingers, instead of under the fist, because it will grant you a more tactile sensitivity to how the horse feels at the other end. However, the "under the fist" position does offer more "purchase" and power.

Jess Ross "ground drives"
Molly and Queenie.

take a deep breath and do it again.

If everything did not go so well let's analyze the possible problems:

A. The horse would not go.

B. The horse wanted to go fast.

C. The horse turned 180 degrees to face you.

D. The horse did not want to stop.

E. The horse tried to get away.

F. All of the above.

G. Something strange happened.

Gosh, if things didn't go well I wish I, or someone with some experience, had been there to see first hand what happened. Away from the situation it is impossible to know all that went into the scenario. This is why I recommend you have someone help you and that you use a well-trained horse to learn. The horse you think is well trained may not be - or you may be doing something to cause irrational behavior on the animal's part. A knowledgeable teamster helping you can quickly identify these conditions.

But lets deal with what we can. Going over our list of possible problems:

A. In your learning situation the safest solution to a horse not

286

starting is to have a helper with a lead rope stand at the animal's head. If it does not move on command the helper should lead it forward and be prepared to unsnap the lead rope and step aside as the horse walks. The experienced teamster will not use this tactic as he or she will have a small bag of tricks - from the use of a whip's <u>light</u> touch to a louder voice - that will get the job done. You on the other hand are learning and <u>DO</u> <u>NOT</u> want to take the risk of spoiling your new relationship with the horse by using too heavy a hand.

Keep in mind that you are dealing with an intelligent animal and he or she may be trying to tell you something by refusing to go.

B. If your horse wanted to go faster than you did and succeeded you were not in control of the situation. Perhaps you had <u>no</u> pressure on the lines or worried the horse. Try again but this time use your most soothing, most calm voice, and ask the horse to "walk" "easy." Do this in little short exercises. This is not a training exercise for the horse - it is a training exercise for you. Don't be afraid to lean back on the lines to slow the horse down <u>if</u> the verbal command is not accepted.

But remember to release that pressure when you are at the speed you want. You may have to repeat this a few times but do so with the "walk" command and soon you'll only have to ask.

If the horse persists, and even seems a little crazy, about going fast, <u>get</u> <u>some</u> <u>help</u>. There are too many things which can figure into the equation the least of which may be that you have to find a different animal to learn with. Better you should learn at this relatively harmless stage that you need a different horse as teacher than to hitch to a vehicle and find yourself running into a tree.

C. This one's easy. If your horse, on the command to go, turns 180 degrees to face you, you either have a completely untrained horse or mechanical failure.

If you have an untrained horse replace it.

If you have mechanical failure first check the mechanic: Did you make (or let) the horse turn around because you had pressure on one line and slack on the other? To answer that question start your horse again and watch to see. Or did you forget to hook both lines to

> ## Bitting Changes.
> *Different bit styles may apply pressures in various ways. If a horse is accustomed to a shank bit with a chin curb strap or chain and is changed to a straight log bit or a snaffle it may take a while for the animal to learn what is required and to respond quickly.*

the bit? If the bit is properly fitted and attached to both lines and there is similar tension/pressure on the lines the horse should <u>not</u> turn around. Did you stay behind the horse or were you pulling from the side? You should always stay behind.

D. The horse that won't stop on command or with line pressure is a hazard. This can be due to lack of training. It could be due to an unfamiliar and lessened bitting situation (see

Bitting Changes side bar). This could also be due to a touch of a panic on the animals part. However, it is the contention of this author that a well trained horse does not easily fall prey to the call of panic. Nothing we have asked the horse to do should cause such a reaction. In workshop situations I have often watched new students ask their horse to stop with a tentative repeated "Ho? Ho?" rather than an assertive "WHOA." I'm not calling for a shout, it's not the volume as much as it is the tone. You should mean what you say and follow it with proper pressure (and resulted release) if necessary.

E. If your horse tried to get away <u>GET</u> <u>HELP</u> and find another horse to start learning with.

Stopping Your Horse.

I've already mentioned what I consider to be the importance of verbal commands over line commands. From the very beginning of your learning try to practice "asking" your animal(s) to stop <u>before</u> making them stop. If they stop <u>on</u> request pulling back on the lines will become unnecessary and you'll be on your way to an "accepting" relationship with a lot of important options.

F. If your horse tried all the tricks you need to find another one to learn with and plan to have the first one trained or culled.

G. Something strange happened? Find someone to describe your situation to or better yet have them come and watch a repeat performance. It is probably wise, at this stage in your experience, to trust your intuition it says "something is <u>very</u> wrong here."

Let us assume for the sake of this writing that you had a successful first session with ground driving (or, if not, the problems have been corrected). Return to your harnessed horse and in the same pen area, once again start your horse in ground driving fashion. This time you will try for some precision. Drive your horse in a perfectly straight line to a predetermined stopping point. After you have stopped take a minute to judge how well you've done. Did you let the horse wander? Did you stop short or long of your point? Now, staying behind the animal, attempt to turn him or her 180 degrees in the smallest possible space and once again drive in a straight line to the point at which you started. How did you do? Perhaps the next step will help you to judge yourself and refine your skill with this simple exercise. If you're driving on dirt scratch an X at the starting point and scratch a straight line in the dirt along the course

Your training that animal all the time.

Everything you do with a horse, allow a horse to do, prevent a horse from doing, and share with the animal, is a piece of training.

you've been working your horse. At the end of the line scratch another X for the second stop and turn spot. (If you are working on sod or some other surface you can draw lines or use string, rope or some other demarkation.) Now that done try your hand at driving your horse right alongside of that line. Imagine you are cultivating a lovely crop and that the line represents

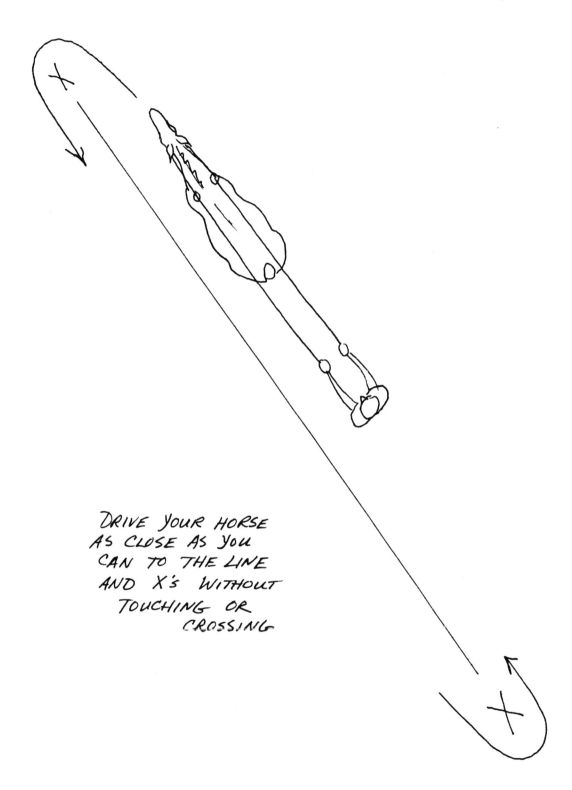

DRIVE YOUR HORSE
AS CLOSE AS YOU
CAN TO THE LINE
AND X'S WITHOUT
TOUCHING OR
CROSSING

the merging plants. You need to be up close to it without stepping on it. And when you reach the X's stop short of stepping on them and practice turning around them close and tight, but without touching the X.

This might seem silly and basic but I guarantee it is an important first step exercise in developing driving skills.

Next please drive your horse down the line, astraddle of it, once again as straight as possible. Do this several times until it becomes easy for both of you.

After that, drive your horse to the middle of the line and turn 90 degrees and go a few steps away from the line. Now, gently, apply even pressure to both lines and say the word "BACK." If the horse comes back release the line pressure and say WHOA. Practice this a few times until you feel ready for a little precision. From that position at a right angle to the straight line back your horse up to, but not over, the line and stop. You may find that stopping the backing horse is confusing. At first it is. See the side bar on "Stopping the Backing Horse." Patience and careful repetition will result in success.

As you do these first exercises and realize some success, share your good feelings with your work mate. Pat the horse's neck and thank him or her for their part. Small gestures such as this do add to the building relationship.

No matter how successful this first exercise may have felt I encourage <u>not</u> to drive the horse out of the exercise enclosure. When you've finished these first steps tie up your driving lines (see **Tieing Up Lines** side-bar) to one hame and fasten a lead rope to the horse to remove him or her to the barn or unharnessing area.

Once you have completely unharnessed and curried and watered and fed your work mate you can slip into satisfaction.

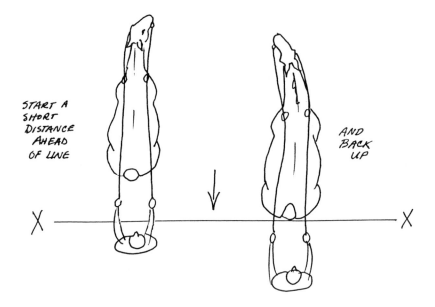

START A
SHORT
DISTANCE
AHEAD
OF LINE

AND
BACK
UP

Tieing Up Lines

These photos demonstrate one way to fasten up, or tie up driving lines. In this case this is one half of a team line. But the same system will work fine with one of a single horse's lines.

Coil up the end of the line in two or three loops, depending on thickness of leather, and fold.

Then pass the folded end of the looped lines through the top hame ring and open loop.

Now pass the opened loop over the hame end and pull down.

This keeps the lines organized and flat and easy to get to. When you go back to the harness rack to pick up that rigging you'll be glad the lines are neatly out of the way.

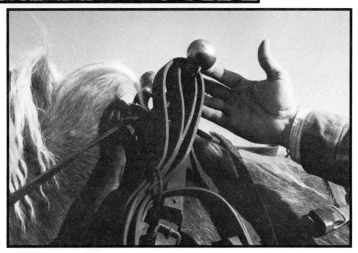

Driving the Team - Beginning Exercises

(Please see page 280 **"Dynamics of Driving a Team of Horses"** to make certain that you understand how team lines are arranged and how they function.)

If you have come straight to this point, passing the section immediately preceding on "Driving the Single Horse" and you have no previous driving experience, please go back and at least read the single-driving section. Many of the points made there are also important to the complete understanding of driving a team.

Quickly, I repeat:

1.) Do these exercises with quiet well-trained horses or mules.

2.) Understand what sound starts your team (see page 282).

3.) Make a concerted effort to have a qualified person there to assist you.

4.) As previously described, do these exercises in a perfect, vacant, controlled, fenced area.

5.) Make sure that bits and bridles are properly fitted and that the team lines are securely and correctly fastened to the bits.

First Exercises with Team

The correct fit of collars and harness will not be critical with these first exercises as we will not be asking the animals to pull anything. Take your harnessed team by lead ropes to the exercise pen. Set up the lines. As in the illustration on the next page, go behind the team and take lines in hand, keep arms out ahead and extended with hands about 12" apart. Remember all that talk and those exercises dealing with perfect tension? Now comes your time to realize how important it all was. Back up until there is very little slack and equal pressure on both lines. Watch the horse's ears to see if they are paying attention to you. If not, call them both, individually, by name. When you have their attention give the verbal command to go. Do not shake or slap the lines. As the pair steps ahead, at a walk, just concentrate on staying behind them and maintaining that perfect tension. Your natural tendency will be to "follow" the horses while "pushing" on the lines. You need to hang back just a little so that there is a slight pull on the lines. Don't make the horses have to drag you by the lines. And don't "push" on those lines, allowing slack that confuses your animal partners about where you want them to go. In this manner just move around the pen or enclosure getting a "feel" for the geometry of the relationship. By geometry I mean literally the changing angles that make up the space delineated by you, your arms, the lines and the bits in the horse's mouths (see diagram on page 281).

After a couple of rounds, in a firm, calm, confident voice, say "Whoa" and prepare to pull back on the lines if the team does not stop. (See Side bar **Stopping Your Horse**, page 288).

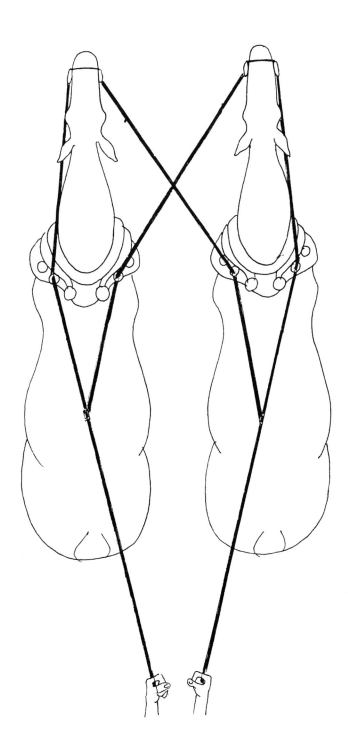

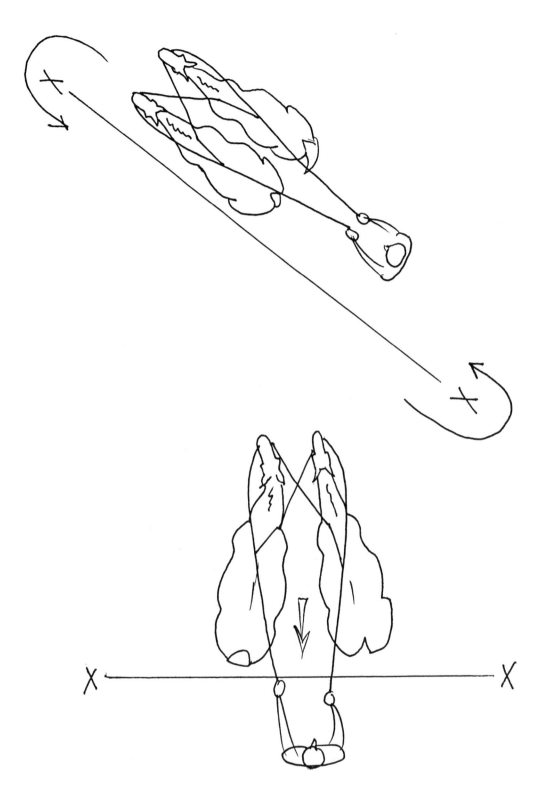

294

If everything worked right, good for you! It was a special thrill, wasn't it? Nothing quite equals that first time you follow a pair of good horses in harness. One thing I always look forward to, in the workshops I teach, is the look on a student's face after that first little drive. So congratulations! Now do the same thing again.

If everything did not go so well turn back to page 286 for a checklist to go over and add these elements to look into:

A. The "team" is three. Two draft animals and you. All three must understand what is expected, allowed, and not allowed.

B. The lines for two horses are more complex. If they are improperly set up it can cause any number of "funny" things to happen (i.e.; horses turn towards each other, horses walk with heads facing out, etc.). If the lines are right the team "should" walk correctly.

C. Equine have personalities which result in likes and dislikes. Two animals accustomed to each other and always working certain sides want things to be "normal." If you are learning you needn't have to deal with the peculiar reactions that will come of altering "normal." Also, putting two strange horses together for the first time may result in sullenness or tantrums that a new teamster is not equipped to handle.

As you may have sensed, driving two horses as a team is not twice as difficult as driving one. In fact, with a good team it can be easier to drive, down a straight line course, because the horses relate to the position and movement of their teammate as well as the bits. Whereas, with the single horse it may require more finesse with the lines to drive a straight line. That said, I do hope that you have correctly sensed from your first little exercise that you can easily get into twice as much trouble with two horses as you can with one.

Only if you had a successful first exercise with the team should you try the next steps. If you were unsuccessful you must come to understand why before you go on. With success, or problems corrected, return to your team in the same round pen or enclosed area. As with the single horse, try driving the team in a straight line to a predetermined stopping point. After you have stopped take a minute to think over how you did. Did the team wander or meander? Did you stop on your mark? Okay, now staying behind the team turn them 180 degrees in the smallest, shortest space and once again drive in a straight line to the point at which you started. How'd you do? Maybe you need a way to better measure your effort. Draw a line in the dirt or lay out a string in a straight line. Drive the team alongside this line, close around the end, and back down it working to keep them close without stepping on or over it. Do this a few times, you'll find it quickly gets easier. But you can't take all the credit. The horses deserve a fair chunk. The reason is that horses appear to gain comfort from easily recognized patterns or repetitions. They will quickly pick up that they are expected to walk alongside the line. Life and work has just gotten a little easier because they know what is expected of them in this simple routine. Later on if you get to doing farm field work with them, and I hope you do, you'll find this to be dramatically true. It is an aspect of working horses that you need to understand,

Driving The Team: Beginning Exercises

A. When you first start your team you need to keep your arms out in front of you and hands about twelve inches apart. Notice the tension on the lines.

B. Stay behind your team. If you keep your arms extended and hold the lines, you can affect a turn by moving sideways behind the horses. Your changing position will change the position of the bit.

C. Layout a string or scratch a line and practice ground driving your team alongside and straight.

D. At the end of the row mark an X or setup a stone and practice driving around it as close as you can.

E. & F. After you have successfully driven down the line try straddling the line.

G. (Above) Set your team so that you are a short distance ahead of the line and give a verbal command to "back" coinciding with a pull on both lines.

H. (Above Right) Just as soon as the horses begin to back release the line pressure and prepare to say WHOA. Try this until you can back right up to the line without stepping over it. You may have to use a brichen rope (see chapter twelve of **Training Workhorses**).

I. Unhook one tug or trace and let it hang while you ground drive your team. This can be helpful in determining how quiet and accepting your horses are. It will make you think about other things as you struggle to figure out how to handle the lines.

297

accept and learn to modify or moderate to your own benefit.

Next try having your team straddle the line, one horse on each side as you walk down the line. You may experience some little confusion or resistance on the teams part. This stems from what was mentioned above. They think they had it figured out, now you must convince them of a necessary change in the routine. A steady, non-punishing, insistence with the lines will accomplish this. Make them go where you want them to.

With that exercise mastered it's time to learn to back the team. Gently, evenly apply pressure to both lines and say the word "Back" in a clear, confident voice. Just as soon as the team begins to lean back, even before a step is taken, decrease the line pressure. After a step or two backwards say "Whoa" and release all line pressure. Do this a half dozen times. If you are confused refresh your memory by reading the side bar "Stopping the Backing Horse."

Now position your team at a right angle to the line you were previously using as a driving guide. With their backs to the line drive them ahead 2 feet and back them up as close as you can to the line without stepping on or over it. Repeat. Repeat.

After doing the backing exercises drive your team, casually, around the pen to loosen you and them up. While still in the enclosure unhook the lines from the bits and set up lead ropes on the pair. Tie the lines up on the harness and lead the team to the barn for unharnessing, currying, watering, feeding and thanks. Now relax and think about it all for a bit.

Stopping the Backing Horse.

Up until now you've been learning that stopping the horse often requires pulling back on both lines. Stopping the backing horse requires the opposite. All pressure on the lines should be released as "WHOA" is said. If this fails to stop the backing horse a command to go forward should be given to reverse the direction of travel. Immediately following the command to go ahead say WHOA and be prepared, only then, to apply line pressure.

Wingers and the Anxious

I wasn't there so I don't know how you did handling the lines but I've witnessed quite a few starting teamsters so I'll hazard a guess that you may have experienced at least a moment of uncertainty about where to have your arms and how to deal with the lines. The early exercises we did with the springs, doubletree and trike should have helped somewhat, but it's not quite the same as having horses ahead of you.

For the purpose of education I will generalize and exaggerate by saying that you need to keep your arms straight ahead and about 3/4 to 7/8's extended and your hands about 12" apart unless crossing-over to pull in slack. If your arms are folded up or bent (see illustration next page and photos following pages), and near or against your chest, you do not have the full advantage of the arm's length for pulling up lines quickly should you need to. It is also quite difficult with arms folded (or bent) to maintain a perfect tension. Those people who

Side Bar: Handling the Lines

A. Arms ahead, hands a foot apart. Until you learn the craft keep the lines between your fingers as shown. This gives you a mechanical empathy for the bit in the horse's mouth. Notice the equal tension on the lines.

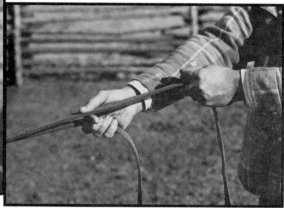

B. To gather in slack, or for making a sharp turn, keep one arm extended, pull in slack with other arm, and take both lines in the one extended hand.

C. Reach forward with the free hand ...

D. ...take hold of the line. Pull that hand back even with the other hand and allow the line to pass through your fingers, if you need to, in order that there be an even tension.

Often times the beginner will freeze up on the lines, afraid to move the hands around, or pass one line to the other hand for even a second. It's almost as though these were life lines and a person feels like they'd fall if they let go.

Side Bar: Handling the Lines

E. After the lines are adjusted for even tension, by gathering and sliding, and the turn is NEARING completion prepare yourself to return to a straight course or whatever other manuever you anticipate.

F. Reverse your previous line manipulation. Pull the line back and take both lines in the one hand.

H. Until you are back to the main driving position.

G. Reach forward with the free hand and take hold of the one line pulling it back, with a commensurate slide...

How you will eventually come to "handle" the lines will depend on your experience and comfort. And it will be a signature of your driving style as well as a strong indication of the relationship you enjoy. In some formal driving circles there is a formal etiquette and posture to handling lines, and it is quite different from what you see here.

Side Bar: Awkward Beginnings With The Lines

WORK TO REPLACE ALL OF THESE NATURAL REACTIONS WITH A MORE EFFECTIVE LINE HANDLING POSTURE.

A. (Left) "Winging." When your arms are out like this you might get some momentary sense of having affected the horse's position but you are, at this very moment, out of control. You have sacrificed all subtlety and finesse and traded it for the posture of one who tells fish stories.

B. (Right) "Casting." This is just as bad as winging, perhaps worse. With each of these exaggerated body moves you will require more time and movement to put yourself back into a position of control. The position of control is a simple relaxed forward position with both arms extended straight ahead.

All of the photos on this page are further examples of problem postures and line handling positions. With each of these the would-be teamster has forfeited his or her control over the team or horse. Whether the problem is slack line(s) or awkward positioning, or a combination of both, doesn't matter. Being out of control matters.

Awkward Beginnings with the Lines

If you find yourself in these positions you are not alone. Most people start here and work towards simple forward posture.

"chest" their lines or fold their arms up close to the body are quite commonly very <u>anxious</u> and nervous, if you could feel their fists and the muscles in their arms they'd feel tense and hard. Extending the arms seems to help to relax the beginning teamster somewhat. And relaxation is important to the fluid movement that usually proceeds success.

Another common posture problem with the lines belongs to those we call "wingers." These people find themselves naturally attempting to take up the slack in one or both lines by holding their arms out and back as if they were wings. This position doesn't work because it, as with "chesting," denies a range of response naturally available if arms are extended straight ahead and hands are close to one another.

Dirk Scholz drives Tuck and Barney on the buck rake as Lynn assists
with the learning curve.

Chapter Five

Secondary Driving Exercises

Don't try anything suggested in this Chapter until you have completed all of the previous training text and exercises.

These next exercises may be done with one or two horses. I will speak to the differences specific to either as it is pertinent.

If you had an opportunity to look at photos or video of your previous (and initial) exercises you might see some evidence of awkwardness in how the lines are managed and how you follow the animal(s). This is to be expected. Now I want you to concentrate on correcting this "driving posture and line handling" because it does affect overall performance.

Remember the discussions about subtlety in line handling, perfect tension, and keeping arms outstretched and hands close together. In your safe training area, once again start your horse or horses and watch your arms and hands. With both arms fully extended, and hands 12" apart (and no "belly" in the lines) follow the animals(s) as you start out. Now, immediately begin to walk, sideways, to the right and keep your arms straight ahead and pointed at the rear of the horse(s). There must be no slack in the lines and the horse(s) should continue moving (see diagram) as you continue to the right. Do not change the tension in either line, keep it the same and keep watching your arms and hands. Now stop. Did you notice what was happening with the horse(s). A turn to the left was occurring and all because your physical position (not the line pressure) was changing as you moved to the right. This exercise demonstrates how subtle and sensitive the dynamic of bit position is. It demonstrates how little change is required to initiate a turn. And it demonstrates that your arms do not need to move away from in front of you.

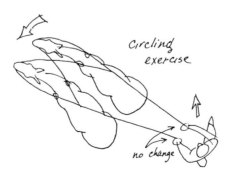

circling exercise

no change

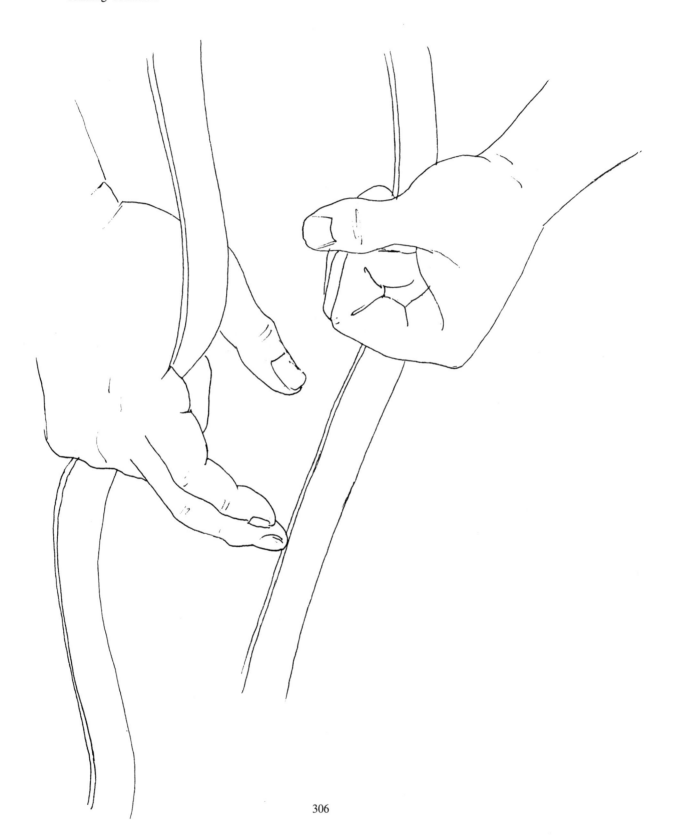

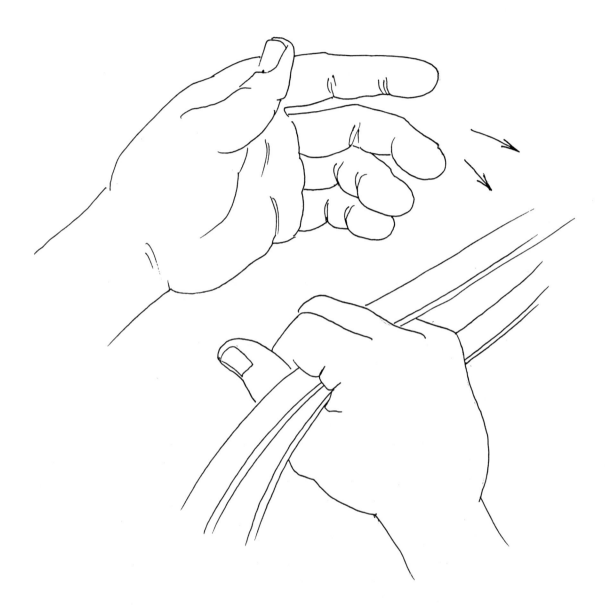

For the next exercise set up three small objects (like empty cans or rocks) on your driving area approximately ten feet apart and in a triangular order (see diagram).

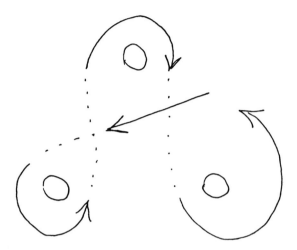

Please ground drive your horse(s) around these objects in the pattern diagrammed without stepping on the objects. The first two times around this pattern attempt to complete it by minimum change in line pressure. Turn your horse(s) by walking the opposite direction as in the previous exercise. The second two times around this pattern, and only if you are in a restricted ideal area, let down one tug (or trace) of your horse's harness and allow the chain to drag. This gives the animal(s) something new to think about and will (or should) wake you up as well. Should this variation cause some excitement stay calm and matter of fact, speak to your horse(s) in a reassuring tone and be prepared to stop whenever control begins to slip. Once you have stopped, stroke your horse(s) and talk to them. But don't wait too long before starting up again. Notice that your partner(s) may step on a tug chain in this exercise, that's okay. (Again, these exercises are offered with the insistence that you be using trained horses!)

Now put the tug chains back up and drive around the course in a circle, once to the right and once to the left, and then enter and complete the course one last time.

Congratulate yourself and your horse(s).

At this point, and because this is a book - quite distant from your experience, I can only hope that some things are starting to make sense to you.

If you are completely alone in this experience (I mean without human assistance) you must be honest with yourself. If you are feeling uncertain or confused, go back and repeat all these exercises until you feel you are beginning to trust yourself and your horse(s). The next steps in your learning curve are high, you must be prepared for what follows. The harness and collar will need to be strong and fit properly. Please see shapter four of *Training Workhorses* for harnessing information. Also refer to **The Work Horse Handbook** for greater detail.

If you are serious about this learning business and determined, or forced, to try it on your own, for the sake of safety you need to make some investments before you continue. One is a stoneboat or worksled. A simple plan is offered in the **Work Horse Handbook**. Variations are fine as long as you understand a few key points. First, the frame must be very strong and that includes the point of hitch. Second, (if using a team) the tongue is an important feature - later, with experience, you may find it is suitable to work without one but don't try it now. Third a headboard, or footboard or some way for you to balance yourself is critical in the beginning (and rest assured that this stoneboat will come in very handy when you start using horses regularly.)

The Stoneboat exercise

I'll try to describe an ideal work area for this next exercise and trust that you will use your intelligence and imagination to come up with your best option.

Four or five acres or more of fairly level, fenced, short pasture with no holes, obstructions, or hazards would be an excellent site.

Single horse

If you are all alone you will have to trust your own estimation of the pulling capacity of the horse you are using to learn with. A horse can, in a moment of extreme exertion, pull far more weight than would be comfortable or safe for sustained work. Just as a human can lift more weight in a moment's passion than it can carry over time, it is also true with the horse. So just because your horse gives its all and is able to pull the stoneboat, don't presume all is as it should be. If your horse must strain to pull the stoneboat, it is too heavy for your driving exercises or sustained work. A full sized draft horse in good flesh, and moderately good working condition, will be able to pull you and a 4 foot by 8 foot wooden stoneboat with 3'" x 12" wood runners (steel lined) with head board and side boards. This load may be a little tuff for a saddle horse or draft pony. Making the sled a little shorter and/or narrower and using lighter weight but equally strong materials will make a big difference. The surface on which the stoneboat is to be drawn makes a big difference. Snow or short pasture grass are the easiest surfaces to pull on. A wet hard-packed dirt can be smooth going. Gravel, pavement and dry dirt are next hardest. Deep mud can be the most difficult. Cold conditions can freeze runners to the ground making it extremely hard to pull. Consider all these things and come to your best estimation of whether or not the sled you will use matches the horse you are learning with.

If you are learning with one horse you will be hooking direct to the stoneboat without a tongue. As long as the area you will be driving in is flat this will work okay. If, however, you are pulling the sled downhill on a slick surface your inexperience could result in the sled running up on the back legs of the horse. This could injure the horse or cause it to try to get away. Make certain you don't allow this to happen. (If you have followed the guidelines for construction of the stoneboat its weight will be sufficient, with you as passenger, to prevent it from running ahead on its own.)

Caution sidebar

Knowing Your Horse

Before commencing with these exercises you need to reassure yourself that your horse is, or your horses are, well trained. If you have any uncertainty or question on this matter DO NOT do the stoneboat exercise. To help answer the question here is an exercise you might try in the original enclosed learning area, one horse at a time. As diagrammed, fasten a single tree with center grab hook to the ends of the trace chains. Wrap and fasten a light chain or rope around a wooden fence post or stick of lumber 4" to 6" thick and 6' to 8' long and hook to the single tree. Stand a little to the side or back behind, out of the path of the post, and give the horse the command to go. If the horse proceeds calmly, drive around in a circle pulling the post. If the horse immediately becomes frightened, calmly stop him - wait until he relaxes and start again. If he remains excited, stop him, talk to him and stroke his neck. Now try it a third time. If he pulls the post successfully and always stops when asked, it is a fairly good indication of acceptance and training. If, however, he gets spooked out of control, is hard to stop, whirls around or absolutely refuses to pull the post, you must not proceed with this animal until it has received some training.

Be cautioned: (Ignoring this warning can result in dangerous situations and possibly physical harm.)

Team

If you are learning with two horses, you will be hooking to the stoneboat with a tongue. This apparatus will prevent any possibility of the stoneboat running up on the rear of the horses. For this reason there is less safety concern that the exercise area be flat, though for your learning it would be helpful. ***All important side note:*** Make sure you are using an appropriate strong neckyoke with harness properly rigged to receive it. If the neckyoke comes loose or breaks you have lost the safety dynamic of the tongue. The neckyoke works best if it is the same length as the double tree.

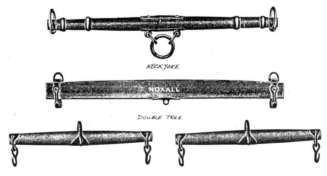

NECK YOKE

DOUBLE TREE

Hitching to the Stoneboat
The Single Horse

Ground drive the horse up to the stoneboat and allow him, or her, to look at it and even sniff it if they wish. Now drive close by and at a right angle to the stoneboat turning sharp when centered.

You might have to back up a little. When the horse is close enough to hitch without any tension on tugs or traces stop and stroke your horse.

With lines in hand and loose, hook the trace chains at the last link to the grab hook single tree.

Driving the Single Horse on the Stoneboat

After this, hook the single tree into the stoneboat hitch ring (see diagram). Now, with lines still in hand and relatively loose, climb onto stoneboat and brace yourself, or balance, so that forward motion of the stoneboat will not cause you to lose balance and lean or fall back on lines. (This will abuse the horse's mouth and maybe startle it.) Absolutely no passengers on the stoneboat with you. Carefully and casually gather up the slack in the lines and give the command to go. If everything works right proceed, in a straight course, for something like 50 feet and then stop. If instead, things do not go right here's a short sample checklist of possibilities. The variety and complexity should go far to illustrate why you need an experienced teamster assisting you. (These will also apply to the stoneboat team exercise). You may find yourself referring to the training workhorses portion of this text.

Caution repeated: The inexperienced person should not attempt to train a work horse.

A. **The horse started the stoneboat a few inches and stopped, refusing to proceed.** Possible explanations:

1) The horse is not accustomed to pulling a load. It is possible to have a horse that is well trained but has no experience displacing a significant load. Horses used for show and carriage purposes might fall in this category. Forcing the horse could create a serious behavior problem called "Balking".

Solution: If this is indeed the problem the horse will need to be gradually accustomed to a load, in which you will have to pass on this horse, or exercise, in your learning.

2. Something is wrong with the harness. A collar too tight or too small, a sharp object pricking the horse as it pulls, some aspect of physical discomfort.

Solution: check fit of harness, run flat of hand under collar and all harness where it touches horse.

3. Most likely - you stopped horse by inadvertently pulling back on lines. This may have happened because the forward jolt caused you to rock back in a natural effort to maintain balance.

Solution: Watch your balance and try again.

4. You have misjudged the weight of you, plus the stoneboat, or some external friction aspect has caused extra resistance.

Solution: Unhook horse from stoneboat and then from single tree. Attempt to lift either end of stoneboat (in cold weather runners may freeze to ground). Check for rocks, stumps, and other obstructions to the forward motion of the sled. How much does your horse weigh? You? The stoneboat? In this exercise a simple rule of thumb would be to keep the weight of stoneboat and driver at 1/2 or less of horse's weight. (This is not a rule for what horses can pull, it is a simple guide or key for this situation.)

B. **The horse jumped ahead and pulled the stoneboat hard and quickly.**

1. Some horses used for pulling competition and in the woods get the bad habit of "jerk starting" a pull and then pulling it fast.

Solution: You, as a student, are NOT equipped to alter your horse's habit patterns. You may have to decide whether your training should proceed with a different horse. (Please see suitable passages in *Training Workhorses.*portion of this book.)

If everything is okay, or you have corrected any problems, proceed to drive for approximately 100 feet but only if you are able to have the horse maintain a walk. **DO NOT PERMIT THE HORSE TO GO FASTER THAN A WALK!** You are not equipped to handle a situation where a walk becomes a trot, which then becomes a lope, which then becomes a full out run. Keep the horse at a walk until you have gained experience.

After you have gone 100 feet and caught you breath be honest with yourself in measuring how well you did, how the horse performed and how strenuous the horse worked. If you feel confident with your performance and handling of the lines, and if you feel the horse is behaving nicely, and if you are comfortable with the load the horse is pulling, drive the stone boat around for fifteen minutes to one half hour. Be mindful that you cannot back this tool, so until you understand some of the dynamics of the overall length of horse and implement, and positioning for turns, stay away from fences and tight spots. Give yourself plenty of room.

Now take a break. With lines in hand unhook the single tree from the stoneboat and then unhook the traces and hang them up on the harness. With your horse either stalled or tied up, go over everything you've done and experienced to this point. Eat a sandwich, take a nap, feed the fish and then return to the driving sight and setup rocks or sticks or pylons (anything you can't hurt) in the course diagrammed below.

You will be hooking back to the stoneboat and driving your horse through this course. Try getting as close as you can to the obstacles without touching them. And pay attention to where the front of your horse is while you're making the turn. Beginners often start their turns too soon and run over the obstacles.

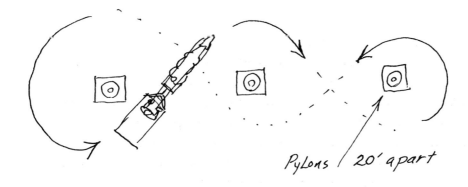

Pylons / 20' apart

Next setup two strings or scratch two lines, or use lime to draw two lines parallel to each other as in the diagram. They will demark an alley through which you will drive. Your object is to run this course without stepping on or over the line or touching it with the stoneboat. The course is diagrammed below.

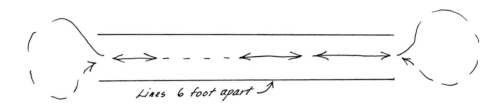

Lines 6 foot apart

Your third exercise course will involve greater precision in your driving. The pattern and course is diagrammed below.

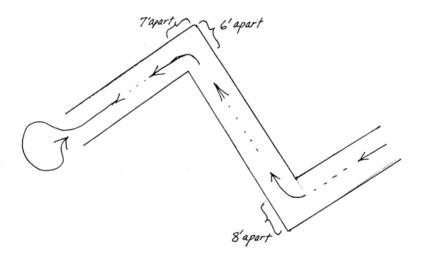

7' apart   6' apart

8' apart

In this exercise you will hopefully pick up on the fact that you can turn your horse, or have him side pass, without moving the stoneboat. This requires that you hold your horse back and turn simultaneously. This effectively changes the trajectory of the drawn stoneboat and will allow you to make sharper corners where there is less room for your horse's extended path. This will be difficult. Don't fret if it takes a bit of doing to get the hang of it. And while you're at it pay attention to your horse. If your experimentations are getting him upset, take a break from the exercise and drive him off in a simple wide circle to allow him to calm down.

Horses are intelligent beasts, and the best of them enjoy the patterns and challenges of work, unless they are being thoroughly confused with contradictory pushing and pulling, and therefore can't figure out what's expected. In such a case they can get cranky or moody. It's best to recognise this and give them something they can understand and appreciate. Please don't think by this that I'm suggesting that they cannot handle complex jobs, they can and do. What I'm saying is that your inexperience might make them lose their temper and willingness. You then need to regain it all.

If you feel confident and somewhat educated to this point you may be ready for the next procedures with a wheeled vehicle. That information follows the team stoneboat exercises.

Hitching to the Stoneboat
The Team of Horses

We are fortunate to have a well illustrated, safe, stoneboat team hitching procedure in the *Training Workhorses* portion of this book (see page 226). I direct you to those photos and offer some additional notes. Although, in the case of those aforementioned pictures, Aden Freeman is taking precautions because he's hitching an unbroke horse, the same safety measures should be taken when you hitch a broke team for your own first drive.

Either a strong fence, hitching rail, or barn wall will do nicely for a place to tie up. You should have your stoneboat parked at a 45 degree angle and so that the neckyoke is within eighteen inches from the tieing-up point. Make sure that the neck yoke is fastened to the end of the tongue, regardless of what style is used. (It is common for a neckyoke ring to slide over the end of the tongue and come to rest against the tongue cap. Use a piece of wire to fasten it there so that it cannot come off - if you have hooked the horses too loose.) Lead your horses out and into position and tie them up.

Here's a simplified hitching checklist:
1. First and always first! Hook up your driving lines. I suggest that you pass the lines, together, back to the stoneboat at this time.
2. Second and always second! Fasten the neckyoke to the breast strap / pole strap assembly.
3. Always last! Hook the tugs to the single trees. If, when you hook the last chain, you see loose tugs, and/or very loose quarter straps, you are hooked too long. Go back and drop one more link on each tug. If, however, when you go to hook the last tug it takes a great deal of force and everything is very tight, go back and add another link. Your hitch is right when there is two to three inches between the quarter straps and the belly when the horses are pulling.

When you tie your horses up, do so with a slip knot that will permit you to untie them quickly and easily. Double and triple check to make sure your lines are set up right. Are the bridle throat latches buckled? Check to see that your neckyoke, pole straps and quarter straps are properly set up.

Driving the Team on the Stoneboat

After you are hitched, step into the stoneboat and sit down (if you have a seat or bale of hay) or brace yourself against the head board and take both lines properly in hand. DO NOT tighten up on the lines yet. Now have someone else untie your horses and step completely out of the way. Now you must steer your team away from the fence and out into the driving area, so you must prepare by pulling in the slack and starting the horses to turn in the right direction simultaneous with your command to go. If things are happening too fast to suit you, calmly stop your team, collect your thoughts, check out where you are and where you are going, and

Another style of stoneboat or worksled. These folks were photographed at the last Holden, Mo,. Small Farm Gathering

restart.

Once you are away from the fence and/or buildings, go twenty to forty feet and stop. Is everything working properly? Are your horses together or does one seem to move its head independently (a sure sign something is wrong with the lines)? Are your horses very nervous? Are you very nervous? If so you may be feeding off each other's nerves. You need to calm yourself and think about something else like homemade ice cream, playing softball, new born foals, homegrown tomatoes, or kissing in the dark. If you calm down, your horses will feel it and do likewise.

If your horses are acting up and you feel uncomfortable, like something bad is going to happen (it probably won't), perhaps you need to trust your feelings and postpone your exercise until you have a skilled person available to assist you. Because, though your horses may be fine, your negative feelings will communicate to them and you may be having some legitimate, or self-fulfilling, foreboding of your inability to handle the situation. Go for safety. If I were there by your side I'd say "let's go for it, everythings gonna be great!" But I'm not, so you have to trust yourself.

If everything's okay, and it probably is, you should drive the team something short of 100 feet making a gradual turn. And make sure that your horses are walking. Do not let them trot or lope or run. WALK THEM! You do that by maintaining a steady pressure on the lines and increasing it to slow them down. If they start to speed up, and ignore your "steady" command and line pressure, STOP. Then restart.

How did you do? Great I'll bet. It was a thrill, I know because it still is for me, and after a quarter of a century!

Catch your breath, take a look at your horses, their harness, where you are in your driving area. Staying away from obstructions, buildings, fences, any hazards, start your horses again and drive a gradual circle. Stop, smile, think about it. Restart your horses and gradually change direction so that you're heading in the other direction. Keeping plenty of room between your outfit and obstructions, just drive around for fifteen minutes to half an hour, stopping occasionally.

Unhitching the Team

Now take a break. You need as much practise in unhitching as you do hitching. So here's the beginner's unhitching checklist:

1. Either tie the horses up to the fence or hitching rail - or have someone stand at their heads prepared to hold them if need be. (Note: Well broke or trained horses will not require this but in the beginning it may be a good idea because you don't know but what you might make a foolish mistake and need the insurance.

2. With lines in hand, unhook the traces and hang them up on the harness. (ALWAYS do this before unhooking neckyoke!)

3. Lay the lines over the side of the horse you pass by, as you go to the front and unfasten the neck yoke. Be careful not to drop the neckyoke and tongue. After it is completely unhooked lower the assembly easy.

4. Now you have a choice, you can either fasten on lead ropes, do up the lines and lead your team away - or you can return to the driving lines and ground drive the team away.

After you have set your horses up safely and comfortably, its time for a cup of coffee or lemonade and a little chat about how it all went. All the more reason to have someone around to help, they can share in the excitement and the instant replay.

After your break, you will be returning to rehitch your team and go through some specific exercises, so first take the time to set up the courses. These courses are the same as those found on pages 313 and 314 except that the dimensions are different. The illustrations are on the next page.

Ready to go? Hitch your team, take the time to double check everything. Drive the team and stoneboat around the slalom course as shown. Practise making close turns around the cones or stones. Avoid stepping on these markers. Pay attention to where the front of your team is as you make your turns.

In exercise number two, drive the stone boat down the alley as straight as you can. Keep repeating until you feel in control.

In exercise number three, drive through this zigzag course practising the same side-pass cornering described in the singlehorse stoneboat procedure on the previous page.

Reread the concerns expressed on pages 314 and 315 regarding your horse(s) temperament and your learning curve.

Hitching to a Wheeled Vehicle
The Single Horse

Once again I must repeat that you need to be working with a well trained horse. And if you are going to hook to a wheeled vehicle it will have shafts and you MUST have someone help you. The procedure I outline here is the same as the one used on page 183 for training a single horse. The precautions necessary are the same.

Within a large open area, selected for your driving lessons, park your vehicle. Take the horse to the cart or wagon and allow him to see it and sniff it. Now, while someone else holds the horse's lead shank, move the cart around in front of the horse. Now circle the horse with the cart, or if it's too heavy and awkward just walk the horse around the vehicle. With one person on the lead rope and one person on the cart shafts, carefully bring the vehicle forward, with shafts raised to avoid contact with the horse until appropriate and necessary. The person on the lead shank should take hold of the shaft tip on his side while the other person moves to the opposite side shaft. Now while still holding the horse, lower the shafts and pull forward and through the shaft loops. Before hitching take down the lines and pass back to the person at the vehicle. Do not pull on the lines unless required to stop the horse. That person holding the lines, you the driver, should fasten the hold-back straps and then the traces. The second person should remain at the head of the horse. The driver should now get on the cart, careful not to lean on the lines, and the person at the head can remove the lead rope and stand to the side available to assist. Give the command to go. Go a short distance and stop. If everything

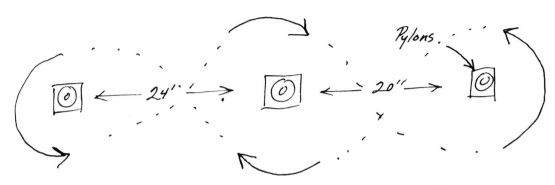

Team Slalom (rocks can be substituted)

TEAM COURSES

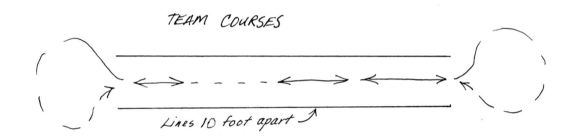

Lines 10 foot apart

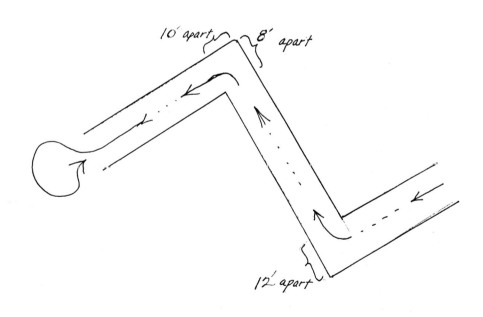

10' apart   8' apart

12' apart

is as it should be, proceed to drive something short of a 100 feet and stop. If all remains well you will be repeating the driving exercises you went through with the ground driving. Setup your courses so that you have plenty of room to maneuver. (Later you can be hard on yourself and tighten the distances for shorter turns and greater precision.) Drive your horse for a half hour to a full hour through these patterns.

If your horse becomes restless or unruly, quit the exercise you're on and simply drive in a gradual large circle. If this does not calm your horse, you should have your helper join you so that you can safely check over the harness and vehicle for any obvious points of discomfort. Check the bridle, the bit, the collar or breast strap, the inside surfaces of the harness that make contact with the horse, the inside surfaces of the shafts, etc. Use common sense. The horse's anxiety may be caused by physical discomfort, lack of training, your own behavior (excessive line pressure, loud voice, general nervousness on your part, etc.), you must trust the early signs and your instincts to determine whether or not you must unhook and get some outside help for proper diagnosis.

If your horse worked nicely and your exercises seemed a little difficult, GREAT, you're on the right path. Now it's time for a break, so you need to follow a safe and specific routine for unhitching.

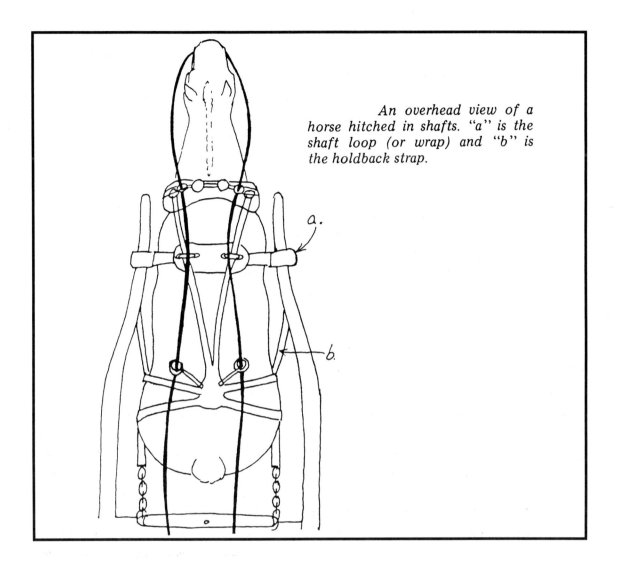

An overhead view of a horse hitched in shafts. "a" is the shaft loop (or wrap) and "b" is the holdback strap.

Have your helper return to the horse's head and snap on a lead rope. Carefully get off the cart keeping the lines in hand and slack. Undo the traces first and hang them up. Keep lines in hand as you go to the opposite side of the cart from you header. While your header releases the hold-back strap on his side, keeping hold of a loose lead rope, you do likewise on your side. Now do up the lines on the hames. While your header holds the horse and guides the shafts from his side, you work the opposite side shaft as you carefully push it back until it is free from both sides. Try not to poke the horse with the shafts or drop them on the ground. Now hold the shafts up as your header leads the horse forward. Before you leave, turn the horse around and let it have another good look and sniff of the cart. And remember to thank you horse.

321

Hitching to a Wheeled Vehicle
The Team

From page 185 of the ***Training Workhorses*** portion of this book there is a detailed routine for hitching a team to a wheeled vehicle. You will be referring to those pages for information on this procedure with the important exception that you should not need to worry yourself about the **buck back rope**. You should be learning with a trained team which does not need this corrective restraint. Those pages go into some photographic detail which we won't repeat here. The only things I will repeat are these cautions;

1. When hitching, always keep the lines in hand or close at hand.
2. When hitching and expecting the horses to stand quietly, DO NOT hold the lines tight.
   The horses will get ansty from this just as you would.
3. When hitching, ALWAYS hook the neckyoke before the evener.
4. When unhitching ALWAYS unhook the evener before the neckyoke.
5. Learn with well-trained horses.
6. If you're alone trust your instincts.
7. If you've got good help doubt your fears.

Side bar:

False Starts

Never allow your horse(s) to start without your expressed command. Whenever you do this you relinquish a piece of your control and dominance in the relationship. You want it understood that the horse(s) will stand quietly until asked to move. NO EXCEPTIONS. It is these sorts of exceptions that will gradually erode the best training.

Once you are properly hitched and mounted on your vehicle drive your team a short distance and stop. Check to see if everything is okay. If it is, proceed to drive for about 3 to 5 minutes in a big circle. If its not okay, look to the previous pages in these last two chapters for indications of why things didn't work. Use your common sense and correct the problem or stop right here and get some help.

Let's plan on everything being fine. Now you can try driving your team through the same exercises you laid out for the stoneboat. Don't fret if it seems difficult at first. Give yourself plenty of opportunity to learn these routines as the experience will help you as you proceed. Stop often and always pay attention to how your horses are behaving and feeling.Spen one half to a full hour on these exercises, then unhook.

Congratulate yourself and your team. But also be honest as to your estimation of how you did. Maybe make a list of the things you need to work on improving. That way you might remember them better next time you drive. Did you keep your arms out in front of you and your hands relatively close together? Did you wing? How did your WHOA sound, wimpy or senatorial? When your team started out did you pull up on the lines and actually cause them to hesitate or stop? Did your team start before your gave the command?

Hitching to a Log
Single Horse & Team

For this next exercise you will need those two logs that were on our equipment list. For simplicity sack I suggested that they be ten to sixteen feet long and 4 to 8 inches in diameter. You will also need the 3/8 inch chain with a sliding hook fastened to one end and a regular hook on the other end (see illustration).

I suggest you try this with both single horses and a team if they are available to you. The dynamics are different and how you must function is subtely changed from one horse to two. For this reason you will need both a single tree with hook and a double tree with hook (as illustrated). If you are serious about possibly skidding logs in the future you may want to make an investment in the manufacture of a good ringed grab hook. For what we are about to do it isn't critical. As shown in the diagram you will be tieing the two logs together with the slide hook end of the chain.

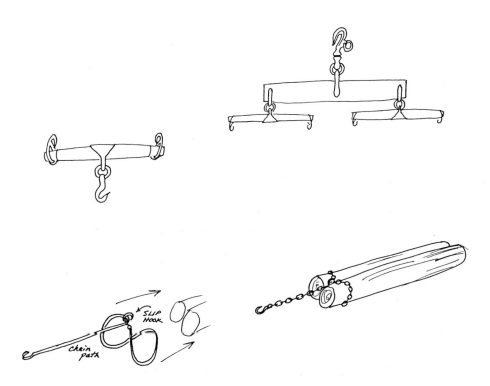

323

In a suitable area setup a slalom course using obstacles which you don't care about or which are unbreakable. At first you will be running the course without the outside barriers lines. After you feel a little arrogant we'll have you add the lines, as diagramed, and try the course again.

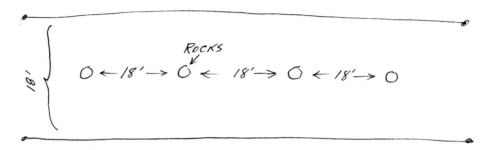

Hook your single horse or your team to the appropriate evener and then to the log chain, about two feet from the logs (as shown).

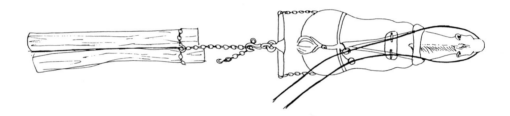

Tieing the two logs together will help to prevent them from rolling over as turns are made, even so as you proceed you need to be evermindful of where the logs are and where they might be in the next few seconds. The logs you'll be working with are small but they can still hurt if you aren't paying attention when they come at your shins on a corner swing.

As you may have guessed your next exercise will involve skidding the two logs through a slalom course. First you will work to avoid touching the "cones". Later you will work to complete the course without touching or crossing a line and without touching the 'cones'.

Back in the seventies the late Monte Rumgay, of Oregon City, came up with this as a competition at the local county fair. After that we used it at our Draft Horse Festival in 1980 and 1981. It has since become very popular and taken off across the continent. We've been employing it as an exercise in our Work Horse Workshops since 1976. It sure helps beginners learn about trajectory and line handling.

The diagrams will illustrate your possible course for the beginning and "advanced" efforts.

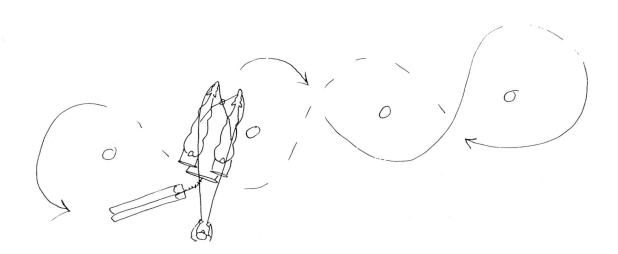

When you first start your horse(s) with the logs hooked on, look out to the point where the horse(s) will step next and back to where the rear of the logs are. When skidding logs you have to develope, as second nature, a constant sense of this full length along with an understanding of what the trajectory of your horse may do to the logs which follow. If you don't get your horse(s) out far enough, before you make your turn, the logs may surprise you by cutting far across the inside of the corner. Running through the slalom will give you a natural sense of what I'm trying to explain.

A student of the Canadian Workhorse Workshops skillfully guides Aden Freeman's team through the log skid obstacle course. Notice he's paying attention to where his logs are.

As you practise this exercise you will want to be able to have your horse(s) move sideways or begin a turn without moving the logs. You will do this by having the horse(s) "sidepass" or "side step". This is accomplished by the subtlest of increased pressures on the lines while you give the command to go. This will take practise. And it is an important manuever to master.

Until you get better on the lines you will probably want to stop your horse(s) and step over the logs whenever you find yourself too much on the inside of the turn. Remember that you need to stay behind your horses. If you should break over to more than a 45 degree angle (as in the diagram) you are approaching that danger zone where your pressure on the lines is being denied by the friction of the angle they must pass through at the hames. This can quickly result in the horse facing you. When you are hooked to logs you don't want this to happen because there is too much that might go quickly towards creating a little wreck. So STAY BEHIND YOUR HORSES and be careful stepping or jumping over the moving logs.

Let's review what you've learned (or been subjected to) so far:

326

A. All that preliminary stuff about how horses work and why anyone would work horses.

B. Information on different approaches to learning the teamster's craft.

C. Harnessing

D. Handling lines

E. Driving the trike and misc. devices

F. Driving the horse(s). Making them stop and go and back and turn.

G. Hitching singles in shafts and teams to stoneboats and wheeled vehicles.

H. Skidding little logs.

If we were in a workshop together I would have tried to lace all of this with all sorts of variables and a healthy discussion about what a magnificent, passionate, intelligent and strange creature the horse is. If you haven't already, please take time to read chapters one through six of the *Training Workhorses* portion of this book.

Since there are so many different types of work you may choose to do with horses we cannot cover them all in the space of this book. I recommend that you at least look at a copy of the **Work Horse Handbook**, it contains quite a bit of information you won't find in this book.

If you've made it to this point with some small semblance of understanding, and if you are still interested in the concept of working horses, we've succeeded!

With what you've learned so far, mixed together with lots of practise and repetition you can apply common sense and actually begin to get some real work done with your horses. And that's what the next chapter is about.

Work horses are best approached as a COMPONENT of a larger system, be it farming or logging or roadwork. This is L.R. Miller on the buck rake and A.E. Miller on the stack.

Chapter Six

Work, Repetition, and Arrival

Where do you go from here? In the format of a book it's hard to go much further without getting into the very esoteric specifics of the adjustment of a certain make of plow or mower - or the operating procedure for spreading manure or compost - or the vagaries of tillage with horses in high altitude sandy soils or muddy clay bottoms - or the advantages of single disc versus hoe drills for seeding - and the frontal arguments about harness design and conformation of work horses. They are all important subjects but much too expansive and diverse to be covered here. That is why we have already begun an effort to cover them in separate titles. This book is number two in what we hope will be a comprehensive Work Horse Series.

Where do you go from here? It is up to you. Permit me to suggest three options.

1. Go to a workshop or seminar (or more than one).
2. Go to work with your own horse(s).
3. Go to work on a farm that uses work horses.

Workshop? I can hear a few of you saying I got this book so I wouldn't have to take a workshop. This book cannot give you what you now need. And that is experience. Experience comes from actual work and repetition, actual doing. And with that you get a skill level that may become the hallmark of you having arrived as a "teamster".

In fact this book has only given you the first little taste of what this grand craft is about, even if you were diligent and successful in all the prescribed exercises. Your vocabulary of response in all things related to work horses is still onlyminiscule. I wish a book could give you more because it would mean yet better circumstances for the horses. But all it can do is point out directions and suggest hazards. The course to "arrival" is all in your hands.

For some of you taking a workshop will be the logical next best step. At the 1993 Work Horse Workshops in Ontario, Canada, I was surprised to see a former graduate, Kristin Hueber, in attendance. In front of the other students I put her on the spot by asking if she was returning because the previous workshop had somehow failed her. She smiled and comfortably answered that she was returning because her first workshop experience had been so positive, so exciting and so full that she was certain she missed important nuances and details. And because she had learned so much from the questions and experiences of the other students. And because she felt that returning would be good for her Shire horse. I learned something from her response. How we advance our learning needn't follow prescription.

But workshops are a general thing and they vary from one part of the continent to the other. So I reasonably expect that a few of you would go on, after the experience of this book, and take a workshop where the instructor(s) vigorously disagree with what you have read here. I think that is good and positive. As I've said throughout this text, there is NO only way. I am for you becoming a skilled, caring, qualified teamster because it will make life better for a few horses, because your success will add a ripple to the growing feasibility of working horses, and because we are all helped by the success of our cultural peers. So if getting there takes you through a place where contradiction is a good teacher, and controversy results in self reliant thinking, we are all winners.

Jimmy Grant, Aden Freeman, and John Male, staff of the Canadian Work Horse Workshops held late-summer each year in Ontario, south of Ottawa. (See resource listing at the back of this book for address information.) The work of these fine gentlemen is recommended without qualification. They are among the best in the craft.

And as for going to work for others I would offer this caution, one that would apply equally to any who go on to workshops; be humble. If you go on to another setting where there are others with experience working horses, experience you may benefit from, nothing will shut them off quicker than you coming across as a brand-new Knowo-It-All. The resident teamsters are the experts. They are the ones who decide how things will be done. You must be respectful, open-minded, and act like a dry sponge - just soaking it all in. Practise safety always, but be humble.

And attend events. Find out where and when the local draft horse shows, farm fairs and plowing matches are held. Check into the draft horse sales. Go to as many as you can and, again, be a dry sponge. You'll be surprised how reading this book will make you feel like you can understand and speak some of the lingo. The experience of watching a truly skilled plowman will mean even more to you now. Watching a top showman ply the lines of an eight-up hitch will command more respect from you after you've struggled with two lines.

Jeb Michaelson, of Oregon, and his fine walking plow team at a 1993 plow field day.

Going to Work with Your Own Horses

I would not be altogether responsible if I didn't forsee and address the fact that there will be some of you who will immediately set off to work on your own. I applaud you for your ambition and sense of purposeful direction. Please allow me to offer up a last set of perimeters and cautions which are general to the work you may do or try.

331

Parades and Taking Your Horse Out in Public

If you have a team of harnessed horses you will be tempted from within, and without, to immediately take them to public events, shows, excursions, drives, etc. And you may want to. Parades, wagon trains, plowing matches and the like can be fun, educational, and inspirational and I encourage you to take part - WHEN YOU AND YOUR HORSES ARE READY! Not before.

Nothing quite makes my skin crawl like a news report of a team of horses running away through a crowd and hurting people. Besides the concerns which might be obvious I cannot help but see this as another needlessly negative piece of publicity for our work horse world. I have even met some non-horse people who are deathly afraid of harnessed horses and believe them all to be powder kegs, time bombs, lit sticks of dynamite, all ready to go off in a minute. Any individual, or club, who has struggled to get liability insurance, for harnessed horses in public, knows that the risk factors are climbing daily. And I said "needlessly negative" because I am sure that 8 or 9 times out of 10 what occurred could have been prevented if the horses and teamster were fully experienced. A good, reliable, well-trained team, or hitch, of intelligent horses can be an absolute joy to share with your friends, neighbors and the general public.

L.R. Miller drives Cali and Lana in the Sisters Rodeo Parade with family and friends aboard. Photo by Judi Knapp

And they can handle crowds, balloons, firecrackers, ferris wheels, sirens, go-karts, thrown candy, terrible arena organ music, as well, and sometimes better than, you and I can.

So how do you know when you are ready? Circumstantial trial by fire. You need to have experienced those little inevitable things (like a covey of quail frightened out of a bush directly in front of your horses, or low flying military aircraft surprising you all, or some piece of plastic or material blowing across your path) and survived them by a combination of your horses' courage and intelligence and your proper timely instinctual response.

Remember you are in charge and have a great responsibility. Your horses can be a weapon or a beautiful contribution depending on your preparedness.

Logging With Your Horses

Horse do a wonderful job of skidding wood products out of forested areas. They can be a piece of a holistic, sustained-yield approach to timber harvest that results in minimum forest floor damage. But logging is more than dragging down trees to a loading site. It is a complex, dangerous, and grueling business. Much work needs to be done investigating and learning the particulars for your area before attempting to make horse logging a life's work.

If you want to skid out a few sticks for firewood, or a chicken house, you may be able

Jerry Harpole, Oregon horse logger, demonstrates his logging arch at a recent field day.

to do that with limited experience behind you, but I urge you to use common sense. Plan a trail. Do your wood cutting before you take the horses in. Do a clean job of limbing. Know where you are going with the material and keep your skid fairly level until you are more experienced.

You should know that one-eighth of a mile is a fairly substantial skidding distance. Any further and you'll want to lift the heavy end of the log to reduce the friction. Many new innovations in the catagory of logging carts and arches, most of them home-made, are rapidly advancing the cause of improved horse-logging efficiencies.

Farming with Your Horses

There are so many procedures and so many pieces of equipment (and combinations of different implements) that we can only barely touch on common practises. To give you an example of the variety, as it might pertain to working horses, here are a few areas of application I am familiar with;

A Percheron mare and a Belgian mare pulling a pasture harrow with a three-wheeled forecart on Singing Horse Ranch.

Vineyard work

Delivery of farm product

Dairy farming

Market gardening

Orchard work

Ranching (cattle/sheep/horses)

Haying

Silage

Composting

Fertilizing

Tillage

Grain handling

Planting

Winter feeding

Excavation

Grading

Root crop harvest

and on and on

Each of these could have different and similar procedural needs. Here are a few observations by catagory.

PLOWING - The walking plow is more difficult to master than the riding plow. Although there are some specific challenges I might hesitantly recommend that the beginner try a two-way riding plow. This tool allows continuous furrows in the same direction thereby eliminating the dead furrows that are hard for a beginner to deal with. If you want to plow you may need to spend some time with others who do - or get some at-home help. Plowing is not necessarily a more hazardous application for horse power. And plowing can be delightful. It still is one of my two most favorite jobs with the horses. I love to see, smell, and hear the turning ground. And you get an immediate sense of accomplishment.

If you think you want to start by using a walking plow, to work up your small garden, you may need to take down the fences at either end of the plot - you'll need plenty of "headland" to turn your horses and plow. For a brief introduction to handling a walking plow refer to **The Work Horse Handbook.** For on-going information on adjusting plows and laying out fields look to **The Small Farmer's Journal.**

GENERAL TILLAGE - When it comes to pulling various harrows over field surfaces you will find you have three procedural choices. 1.) Walking behind the harrow which is hooked direct to the horses. 2.) Using a harrow cart which straddles the harrow and places you behind the tool. 3.) Using a forecart (homemade or store-bought) which runs between the horses and the harrow. If you are uncertain about your skills with the lines but certain that your horses are well-trained, I recommend that you use a forecart. If you are more certain of your skills and less certain of the horses training you may want to use a harrow cart or walk behind.

If you plan on using a disc harrow you need to take some specific precautions. Many discs are pulled without tongues or poles. When the disc is running in plowed or worked ground, and set at any cutting angle, there will be more than sufficient braking action to hold the disc from running up on the horses. However, in transport, over solid surfaces with the discs set straight, the implement may run up on the horses. You do not want this to happen. So pay attention to the grades you will be traveling over and either setup a tongue or pole - or be prepared to transport the disc with an angle set to provide some resistance.

If you are pulling a roller-packer you will need to either use a forecart or setup a tongue, also to prevent this tool from running up on your horses.

If you are pulling a chain style pasture harrow you might be surprised to discover how heavy it pulls. If you are set to work one or two or three horses you may want to do some research before you sink a bunch of dough into a pasture harrow that may end up being too hard to pull. There are many different designs and widths of competing makes and they don't all pull equal commensurate to size. I know one man who spent 300 plus dollars for a ten foot wide harrow and was angered to discover that it was an excessive pull for his team.

SEEDING - For field crops you have a choice of whether or not to broadcast seed and follow it with a harrow and packer - or you can drill the seed into the ground, down to a depth where there may be moisture. There are broadcast seeders which can be mounted on the back of wagons or on forecarts. There are hundreds of different models of drills suitable for use with horses. If you have a drill designed for use with tractors it may have excessive weight in front of the axle which will force you to either setup tongue trucks or pull the drill with a forecart. Greater precision and seeding efficiency can be had with a drill.

For row crops you have a primary choice between one and two row drills. One row drills are single horse tools and are best operated by someone who can drive a horse straight (although they do say there is more corn in a crooked row). Two row drills are operated by a team and although not particularly hazardous, they do require some smarts to operate properly.

There are complex horse-drawn planting and transplanting machines for potatoes and various other crops. Some of these tools require extra people to ride along and set the plants.

FERTILIZING - Manure spreaders, and granular fertilizer spreaders can, of course, be pulled by horses. Manure spreaders are, by nature noisy and active. Because of the clanging of chains and the flying manure you don't want to subject an untrained horse or team to this procedure unless you want to go very fast. A tip; until you get to know the tool and your horse's reaction to it start with a half load loaded near the front. This will give the horse(s) a chance to get to know the vibration and noise BEFORE the manure starts to fly. A manure spreader is an excellent tool to train horses to go into the show ring.

If you need to use a field boom sprayer with horses take the time to let the horses become accustomed to the sound of the spray, the sound of motor, and the feel of the mist before they are ever hooked to the tool.

CULTIVATING - For row crops there are one, two, and four row cultivators which are used by one, two, and four horses. The one horse cultivator has you walking behind. The two row has you riding and the whole affair straddling one row. The four row is a bit out of our range for this discussion. If you are uncertain on the lines you can destroy a lot of young plants in a very short time with a cultivator. Horses, enjoying habit as they do, will quickly learn to walk between the rows and do a splendid job of cultivating. If the plants are tall enough you may have the added hassle of the horses wanting to nibble as they go. A wire basket muzzle is sometimes used for this, but the good teamster can "talk" his horses into leaving the plants alone - and is clever enough to rest his horses at row's end. With a riding straddle row cultivator the operator sits as though in a basket with his feet in stirrups which can help to articulate the steering of the cultivation. Because of this it is difficult for the operator to dismount gracefully and quickly. For this reason the riding cultivator is not a tool to break horses with.

MOWING - Beginners should not attempt to operate a horse drawn mower without qualified help. The mower demands precision in timing and overall setup. Without this it may not operate properly. The mower vibrates and makes a noise that can be very threatening to the uniniated horse. The clipping cutter bar can be EXTREMELY dangerous. The operator of the mower must not only drive the horses, he or she must also be paying constant attention to the operation of the implement.

RAKING - Raking hay can be done by one or two horses, however most side delivery rakes, though easy pulling, operate best with two horses. Tractor rakes which are ground driven can be hitched behind forecarts and used efficiently. The horse drawn side delivery rake has the operator sitting pretty much dead center over the operation. It is a hazardous position to be in as the tool is moving underneath you. Use well-trained horses only.

BALING - Yes, horses can pull self-powered balers. The most popular models are the smaller ones with front mounted fly wheels (i.e., New Holland). These seem to have slightly less thrusting sway to the tongue. You will need to hook to a forecart although I have seen

Tony Miller raking hay with Barney and Molly on Singing Horse Ranch. Note where he is sitting in relation to the machine.

some with permanently mounted tongue wheels. You may find it useful to have some sort of parking brake on the forecart to help alleviate the tongue sway when you are stopped and the baler is still moving. Again to accustom the horses to the tool it is a good idea to have them tied somewhere near the baler as it is in full operation. Allow them to watch it and hear it, even sniff it. This will help them to deal with it being behind them later.

HAY LOADER - I figure if a team is broke for the hay loader they are broke for about anything. I don't know why it is but a clanging hay elevator-loader, pulled behind the wagon the horses are hitched to, drives many horses nuts. You will need a team that can walk slow. And you should be prepared to make some gradual circular corners in the beginning. If you insist on making ninety degree corners the team will have a moment when they can see the loader, off to the side, and they may want to part company. By making gradual corners in the beginning you are giving them a chance to get accustomed to the vibration and the noise before the sight.

BUCK RAKE - Putting up hay loose, in outside stacks, is an important option in the arsenal of some horse farmers. But you have to have an efficient way to move the hay from the field to the hay stack. "Pushing" hay with the buck rake is the way to go. I love to buck rake hay. It is one of the most unusual setups for horse power as you have divided you team into two separate singles. To make a turn you ask one horse to pivot in place while the other horse walks. Because of the complexities this is another job you will need help in learning.

The author bringing in a jag of hay with Cali and Lana. Sometimes you can't even see over the mound of hay and must trust your horses to help guide you.

MISCELANEOUS HARVESTING EQUIPMENT - Grain binders, corn binders, potato diggers, and other specialized tools require so much operating finesse with the procedure that handling the horses must come naturally. If you're on a steep learning curve you'll find these tools a disaster to attempt. They are complex, they demand precision timing and setup, and they also require your full understanding of the readiness of the crop and weather. In other words they will tax your right to call yourself a farmer, let alone teamster. That said they can be exciting as heck to run successfully giving you a feeling as though your are wearing some rightfully annointed crown.

338

John Male with three abreast on his Ontario, Canada, dairy farm binding oats.

The author drives Barney and Molly as they dredge weeds from a pond on Singing Horse Ranch.

FEEDING - Out west one of the long standing romantic applications of horse power is feeding livestock in the winter with a team. Now here's a job that the beginner can go to with a modicum of precaution and preparation.

In the snow we use a heavy bob sled with a flat bed and head board. And when there is no snow a rubber-tired flat bed wagon works nicely. When you have some experience you may be able to fasten the lines to the headboard and feed the hay yourself while the team ambles along through the pasture. But in the beginning you should plan on staying with the lines. You may have some tell you, or show you, that you can get off your wagon, or sled, and move to the front of the horses to open the gate - and after you've got the team through the gate - return to shut it. DON'T TRY IT . With well trained horses and a skilled teamster this can and does occur. But you as a beginner are asking for trouble to try it because you don't know how to read all the little signs yet. I can tell by the look in my horse's eyes whether or not they are worried, anxious, angry, or prankish. It will take you awhile to notice things like that and to know how to behave with the knowledge.

Feeding hay on Singing Horse Ranch

In Summation
How Do You Know You've Arrived?

One day I was returning to the barn, mid-afternoon, on my mower with Cali and Lana. We had just finished mowing the last hay of the season. They knew it and I knew it. We were ambling across the field and I noticed, first, that they were listening to me. Then to my surprise I noticed I was singing, not very well, some dumb madeup song about "heading for the barn 'cuz we'd finished the hay". I heard a hawk screach somewhere over the rimrock. And I saw a sage rat scurry for his hole. The sky was a two o'clock blue and forever deep. I could smell the mare's sweat and I was looking forward to their feeding and currying. I was right where I wanted to be. Comfortable, capable, and a part of something. And even after a quarter of a century I was still doing something that was fresh and enthralling. I was working horses. And not just horses but horses I trusted and admired. And horses that trusted and liked me, several generations of them.

I set out with this book to share that feeling in the most direct and constructive way I could, because I had a grandiose idea of trying to help horses and people I had not yet met. I can only hope...

Stay humble, cautious, caring and enthralled.

L.R. Miller
Singing Horse Ranch, Spring of 1994

L.R. Miller with Tony and Juliette on the feed sled drawn by Cali and Lana.

INDEX

ABOUT THE AUTHOR

Lynn Ralph Miller was born in Kansas City, Kansas in 1947. He received a Bachelor of Fine Arts Degree and two Master of Fine Arts Degrees in Painting. Since 1969 he has resided in Oregon where he has combined farming, ranching, parenting, drawing, painting, writing, and working with draft horses. In 1976 he began, and has since owned and operated, **Small Farmer's Journal** Inc. - a company doing business in alternative agricultural publishing and related research. The primary product of SFJ Inc. is the quarterly **Small Farmer's Journal** *featuring practical horsefarming*. In 1980 he authored the widely acclaimed **Work Horse Handbook**. He has lectured, moderated, judged and taught workshops in various locations across North America. Since 1979 he has produced horsedrawn equipment auctions and trade fairs in Oregon. He has authored and edited several other books. He currently resides on Singing Horse Ranch in a remote high desert area adjacent to the Cascade Mountains where he and his wife, Kristi, and their family, farm and ranch.

When pressed for a self-evaluation he said,

"I am a poor writer that doesn't know when to quit. I am a good husband and father, and an effective teacher, editor, and organizer. Right now I'm looking forward to having the time to get to some work I'm better suited to do. Most of what I've accomplished to date was done because it needed doing and the better qualified people were all too busy."